S0-CAG-630

MARSUPIALS
and
MONOTREMES
of Australia

LYNE, Arthur Gordon. **Marsupials and Monotremes of Australia. Taplinger, 1968 (c1967). 72p il bibl 67-12697. 5.95** *CHOICE* *OCT. '68* *Biology*

Illustrations and descriptions of animals found for the most part only in Australia and adjacent islands. The first section on the monotremes is relatively short, there being only the platypus and the echidnas in this group. The many and varied marsupials occupy the greater part of the book, with a brief discussion as to how they have reached Australia from their site of origin. A drawing of each animal is accompanied by a succinct account of its morphology, range, habitats, feeding and breeding habits, and other characteristics. Thus it resembles somewhat Buffon's classic volumes, while it is better written and arranged than others dealing with a limited group, such as Huheey and Stupka's *Amphibians and Reptiles of Great Smoky Mountains National Park* (1968). More condensed than Pedersen's *Polar Animals* (CHOICE, July–August 1967), lacking any personal reference to the author or his adventures. Concludes with a bibliography chiefly but not exclusively of Australian publications, a strong plea for conservation, and index limited to the animals included. Of value to the taxonomist, zoologist, and those interested in natural history and conservation. Recommended.

268

MARSUPIALS
and
MONOTREMES
of Australia

Dr Gordon Lyne

TAPLINGER PUBLISHING COMPANY
NEW YORK

GORDON LYNE, *B.Sc., Ph.D., is a graduate of the University of Tasmania. In 1953 he joined the research staff of the C.S.I.R.O., and is now at the Ian Clunies Ross Animal Research Laboratory, at Prospect, near Sydney. He is a member of the Australian Mammal Society, the American Society of Mammalogists and a Scientific Fellow of the Zoological Society of London.*

First Published in the United States in 1967 by
TAPLINGER PUBLISHING CO., INC.
29 East Tenth Street
New York, New York 10003

Library of Congress Catalog
Card Number 67-12697

PRINTED IN AUSTRALIA

Contents

Acknowledgements

MANY PEOPLE have been most generous in supplying the photographs used in the preparation of the drawings which illustrate this book. I am deeply in debt to B. J. Marlow, Curator of Mammals, Australian Museum, Sydney; J. Kirsch and Dr G. E. Heinsohn, Department of Zoology, University of Western Australia; R. H. Green, Queen Victoria Museum, Tasmania; Professor G. B. Sharman, Department of Zoology, University of New South Wales; P. Woolley, Department of Zoology, Australian National University; Dr S. Barker, Department of Zoology, University of Adelaide; Dr E. P. Walker, Maryland, U.S.A.; Dr G. D. Brown and T. C. Dagg, Division of Animal Physiology, C.S.I.R.O.; and I. T. Roper, Division of Animal Health, C.S.I.R.O.. J. H. Calaby, Division of Wildlife Research, C.S.I.R.O., kindly read the manuscript.

Monotremes, or egg-laying mammals

THE platypus and echidnas, collectively called the monotremes, are the most primitive of all mammals, and they are entirely confined to the Australian region. No intermediate forms between these highly specialized animals are known, and they so little resemble one another that their relatively close relationship would hardly be suspected. However, both these strange creatures lay eggs from which the young are subsequently hatched. The egg-laying character is considered to be a primitive heritage from ancestral reptiles, but the presence of hair, milk glands, a diaphragm, as well as many other anatomical features, demonstrates that the monotremes are not reptiles but mammals.

The monotremes are intermediate, in many respects, between reptiles and higher mammals. They have a number of features not found in other mammals, but which are usual among reptiles. One of the important differences between reptiles and mammals is seen in the attitude of the legs. In reptiles the legs sprawl out from the sides of the body, whereas in land mammals, as in a cat or a cow, the legs extend vertically below the body, holding it well clear of the ground. The reptilian stance requires an elaborate shoulder girdle. In the monotremes, whose stance is more reptilian than typically mammalian, the shoulder girdle is similar to that of a reptile.

Other interesting reptilian features are seen in the reproduction and excretory systems. In both sexes of the monotremes, as in all reptiles, the intestine, bladder and reproductive organs all open into a common chamber, the cloaca, and there is only one external opening. The penis of monotremes is used solely for delivering sperm and not used also for urination as in all other mammals. The higher mammals have developed separate outlets for the digestive and reproductive tracts. Marsupials are like monotremes in that they have only one opening—a cloaca—but there are large differences in the internal arrangement of these systems. The eggs of monotremes are also reptile-like in that they have large yolks and rubbery shells.

The monotremes are much better equipped to control their body temperature than are reptiles. Except during hibernation, or torpidity, in some forms, the higher mammals maintain a high and constant body temperature, while in reptiles the body temperature varies with that of the surroundings and is never far above or below it. The body temperature of the monotremes, however, does not quite reach that of the higher mammals. It is about 31° to 32° C.; in higher mammals the body temperature ranges from about 36° C. upwards for a few degrees.

There is abundant fossil evidence that the mammals have evolved from reptilian ancestors. Unfortunately, the few fossil monotremes which have been found are of no great antiquity and do not differ from modern forms. Because of this lack of evidence, the evolutionary history of the monotremes is unknown; however, most scientists believe that the monotremes are not closely related to the marsupials and higher mammals, and that they evolved from a distinct group of reptiles.

PLATYPUS (*Ornithorhynchus anatinus*)

The most remarkable of the monotremes, the platypus, is one of the world's most curious mammals. It has a duck-like "bill", webbed feet, a flattened, beaver-like tail, and lays eggs. When the first stuffed specimens reached England more than 160 years ago, they were thought to be fakes, made by sticking together bits of two different animals.

The platypus is an amphibious mammal which grows to about 20 inches in length. It is found in the eastern part of Australia, including Tasmania, where it lives in burrows above the water level of rivers, lakes and water-holes. The fore-feet and hind feet of the platypus are webbed like those of the otter. The webbing on the hind feet reaches to the base of the claws, while on the fore-feet it extends beyond the claws to make extra large paddles, and the platypus depends on these paddles for swimming; on land the excess webbing folds under for walking and burrowing. The claws of the fore-feet are used in burrowing. The muzzle also is used for this.

The somewhat flattened body of the platypus is covered with a dense velvety fur which is dark brown on the back and a paler, creamy-yellow shade below. The specialized muzzle, or "bill", is covered with a hairless, leathery-looking but nerve-filled, skin, which is developed into a shield-like flap close to the eyes. The sensitive muzzle is a very important organ for guiding the platypus while it swims blind and feeds on mud bottoms. It possesses facial furrows that simultaneously close both eye and ear orifices when the animal submerges. The paddle-like tail assists the platypus in diving, and acts as a stabilizer when it swims.

The male platypus has a sharp, horny, poison spur on the heel of each hind foot. This spur is hollow, and connected with a poison gland in each thigh. The poison is not fatal to man but causes intense pain.

The burrows of the platypus are of two kinds. One provides living quarters and in the breeding season is occupied by males only. The other, a nesting burrow, is excavated by the female. This special burrow twists and turns, and may be very long. The nesting chamber is lined with dry grass and leaves, and two or three rubbery-shelled eggs are laid. The eggs, about $\frac{1}{2}$-inch long and cemented together, are kept warm by the mother for 7 to 14 days before they hatch. The young, also about $\frac{1}{2}$-inch long, start to lap up milk which oozes from pores on the mother's belly. After about 4 months the young are weaned, and they leave the burrow for their first swim.

The platypus has an enormous capacity for food. It is said to devour the equivalent of half its own weight each night, the food consisting chiefly of small fresh-water crustaceans, insect larvae and molluscs. Unlike the echidnas, the platypus has teeth when young, but these are replaced by horny plates in the adult.

ECHIDNA OR SPINY ANT-EATER
(*Tachyglossus aculeatus*)

The echidnas also rank high among the world's most interesting mammals. Two distinct species (*Tachyglossus aculeatus* and *Tachyglossus setosus*) are recognized in Australia. The latter is confined to Tasmania and some of the islands of Bass Strait. In addition, different kinds of echidnas occur in New Guinea. The species found on the Australian mainland is widely distributed in habitats ranging from rain-forest to desert and, unlike the platypus, is found in Western Australia.

Although echidnas are well adapted for digging, they do not excavate burrows. They have strong legs and powerful claws which enable them to cling to and sink into the earth, with remarkable rapidity. They push earth out to the sides and sink straight down into the ground.

Superficially, the echidna is nothing like the platypus. It has a rounded body covered with a fortress of sharp spines like those of hedgehogs and porcupines, although it is only very distantly related to these animals. The echidna found in Tasmania has shorter spines and more conspicuous hair than the mainland species.

Like the platypus, the echidna has a long, naked and sensitive muzzle. The mouth is very small, and is sufficient only for the protrusion of the sticky tongue, which with a large echidna can be extended to about 6 to 7 inches beyond the snout. Its food consists almost entirely of ants and termites or white ants, which it obtains by tearing up their nests. The jaws have no teeth, and the food is crushed between hard spines on the tongue, and the roof of the mouth.

The echidna lays one egg into a pouch which develops on the belly only in the breeding season. Just how the egg is placed in the pouch and how long it takes to hatch, no one knows. After hatching, the young one, about ½-inch in length, stays in the pouch and gets its milk by sucking. The young echidna has grown too big for the pouch at about the time the spines appear. At this stage the young animal is left in a sheltered spot until it can look after itself.

Marsupials, or pouched mammals

THE marsupials, or pouched mammals, show an advance on the monotremes, in that before birth the young have already emerged from the egg, though they are less developed at birth than are the higher mammals.

Although the marsupials are represented in certain parts of America, they have their stronghold in Australia, where there is a great variety of peculiar forms. Besides the well-known kangaroos, wallabies, possums and koala, there are many other marsupials. Less known are the marsupial mice, native cats, tiger cat, Tasmanian devil, Tasmanian tiger, marsupial mole, marsupial ant-eater, wombats, rat-kangaroos and bandicoots.

The American marsupials fall into two distinct families, the well-known true opossums (or possums) of North, Central and South America, and the extraordinary rat-like marsupials of South America. It seems probable that America was the original home of the marsupials, but there is insufficient evidence to decide whether they originated in North America and spread southwards, or South America was the home of the group.

By what route did the ancestral marsupials reach Australia? Some scientists favour an entry from the north over a land-bridge which may have connected Australia to Asia. The weak point of this theory is that no remains of ancient marsupials have yet been found in Asia. The opposing view is that the marsupials entered Australia from the south. It has been suggested that Australia and South America were connected at one time by land-bridges with the Antarctic continent which, at an earlier period, must have had a milder climate.

The marsupials have been able to adapt themselves to a great variety of widely differing modes of life and they have exploited every available habitat. Thus there are burrowing forms—the marsupial mole, the wombats, and the rabbit-eared bandicoots; terrestrial forms—the rat-kangaroos, wallabies, kangaroos and most bandicoots; arboreal forms—the possums, the koala and tree-kangaroos; gliding forms—the feather-tail glider and sugar glider; and even, in South America, an aquatic species. Marsupials may be insectivorous, carnivorous, herbivorous, or mixed feeders.

Many of the marsupials show a remarkable resemblance to certain of the higher mammals without being closely related to them. Popular recognition of this fact is recorded in such names as "native bear", "native cat", "tiger cat", "Tasmanian tiger", and so on. An outstanding example is the marsupial mole (*Notoryctes typhlops*) which in almost every external feature resembles the true moles of Europe and Africa. The marsupial mole is one of the most remarkable of the specialized marsupials. It has no eyes or ears and it lives almost entirely underground. Of the many other examples a few must suffice. The tree-climbing possums and the koala may be compared with lemurs, monkeys and sloths of other continents, and the gliding possums may be compared with the "flying" squirrels. Some of the marsupial mice, bandicoots and wombats resemble some of the true rodents. The numbat or marsupial ant-eater, the honey possum and the pig-footed bandicoot are among the animals showing extreme specialization. The numbat for example, besides lacking the characteristic pouch, as do a few other marsupials, has a long tongue and other features specially adapted for gathering and swallowing ants. The honey possum is peculiar among the marsupials in that it feeds with its long bristle-ended tongue on the nectar of flowers. The remarkable pig-footed bandicoot has fore-feet which resemble those of cloven-hoofed ungulates, such as deer, sheep and goats, and hind feet which show a rough similarity to solid-hoofed ungulates, such as the horse and zebra. Another highly specialized marsupial, the tree-kangaroo, has succeeded in re-adapting itself from a jumping to a tree-living existence.

Although precise information on the distribution of many of the Australian marsupials is lacking, it is known that a number of species (mostly members of the kangaroo family) have become extinct within historical times. Other species, including some very interesting forms, like the Tasmanian tiger and the pig-footed bandicoot, have disappeared from many of their old haunts, and it may be too late to save them from extermination. Fortunately, however, most marsupials are now wholly protected by law; and more naturalists and professional biologists have become actively interested in the conservation of the native fauna.

The interest attached to the monotremes and marsupials has appealed to many scientists so strongly that they have often neglected to pay much attention to the higher mammals native to Australia. In fact, it is a popular error to suppose that all native Australian mammals are monotremes or marsupials. The higher mammals are represented by the dingo, a number of bats, a variety of rodents and various marine forms, such as the seals, the whales and the dugong. No large land mammals, such as lions, tigers, elephants, rhinoceroses, camels, buffaloes, and many other groups which are present in other parts of the world, are native to Australia. Such of these as are present arrived through the agency of man.

Marsupial Mice

There are about 30 kinds of marsupial mice in Australia, some as big as rats. Marsupial mice are different in many ways from ordinary mice, which are rodents. The possession of 8 incisor teeth in the upper jaw, and 6 in the lower, immediately separates these small marsupials from the true mice and rats which have only paired gnawing incisors.

BROWN MARSUPIAL MOUSE (*Antechinus stuartii*)

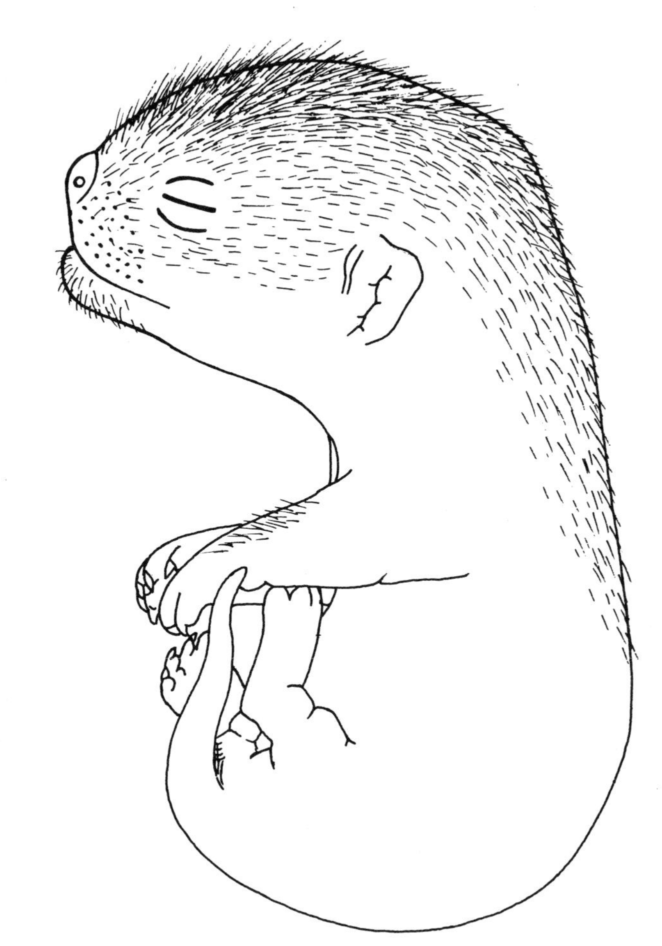

This marsupial mouse is found on the eastern side of Australia and is common near Sydney, where it lives in caves in the rock outcrops of the Hawkesbury sandstone country.

It is on the move at night and is extremely fast and agile. The natural diet consists mainly of insects and other invertebrates, although carrion is also eaten.

There is only one breeding season each year. Litters of up to 10 young are born in August, September, or October, after a gestation period of approximately one month. The new-born baby is very small, being only 5 mm. ($\frac{1}{5}$-inch) in length. The baby illustrated is older, being about 15 mm. long and with distinct ears and emerging hairs. There is a very marked front to rear gradient in the appearance of the hairs in this little marsupial. The pouch young are firmly attached to the teats until they are 5 weeks old. At 10 weeks they may ride about on the back of the mother, retaining their position by gripping the hair with their teeth and fore-feet. The young are weaned when 4 to 5 months old and reach sexual maturity in the year following their birth. Males become senile after one breeding season but females can produce litters in at least 2 successive breeding seasons.

BYRNE'S MARSUPIAL MOUSE (*Dasyuroides byrnei*)

Byrne's marsupial mouse was one of the most interesting animals discovered by the Horn Expedition to central Australia in 1894. During daylight hours it inhabits burrows in the stony gravel plains or gibber deserts near the junction of South Australia, Northern Territory and Queensland. Its size is nearer to that of a rat than a mouse, and in general appearance it resembles the crest-tailed marsupial mouse, but the hind feet have only four toes, as in some of the native cats.

The pouch, which is only very slightly developed, encloses 6 teats, and the litter size is up to six. The young are born when only 4 mm. ($\frac{1}{6}$-inch) in length, after a gestation period of 32 days, and they are mature in all respects at the end of 12 months.

FAT-TAILED MARSUPIAL MOUSE (*Sminthopsis macrura*)

This very attractive ground dweller is widespread throughout inland Australia, where there are open grassy woodlands. During the day it nests under rocks or in hollow logs, and at night it ventures forth to feed mainly on insects.

It has a sharp fox-like face and large ears. It is an aptly named marsupial mouse in that it stores fat in its tail to withstand times when food is scarce. When insects are numerous the tail is well-padded, but when the living is not so good, the tail is thin.

TUAN OR BRUSH-TAILED PHASCOGALE
(*Phascogale tapoatafa*)

This attractive rat-sized species, distinguished by the brush of long black hairs which surrounds the terminal three-quarters of the tail, was one of the earliest marsupials to be observed round Sydney. It has a remarkably wide range as it is found on the eastern side of southern Queensland, New South Wales and Victoria. It is also recorded from the south-east of South Australia, Arnhem Land in the Northern Territory, and the north and south-west of Western Australia.

The tuan lives in wooded and forested country, where it nests in hollow branches. It is an agile climber but seldom seen, for it is about only at night. The food of the tuan includes insects and small vertebrates such as lizards, birds and rodents.

MULGARA OR CREST-TAILED MARSUPIAL MOUSE
(*Dasycercus cristicauda*)

This compact little animal inhabits the arid part of central Australia, where the average rainfall is 5 to 10 inches a year. It is considered to be a typical inhabitant of the Centre, where it is one of the commonest small mammals, even in the most arid areas. It lives on a predominantly or exclusively carnivorous diet, with insects, small reptiles and small rodents its chief food items. Captive animals can get all the water they require from a diet of laboratory mice and fresh lean meat, if they do not have to use water to cool themselves. The mulgara is reported to be absolutely fearless and it attacks a house mouse with lightning speed. During the plagues of house mice, recorded in the Centre, these marsupials have cleared them from certain districts in a remarkably short time.

The tail of this desert dweller is usually thickened at the base, and there is a terminal crest of coarse black hairs on the upper surface. Mulgaras shelter in small burrows in sandy country covered by spinifex. In this way they avoid the heat by remaining underground when the outside temperature is high.

The breeding season in South Australia is said to be from June to September and there are usually 7 young in a litter. The gestation period of a captive female in Queensland, which produced a litter of 6 young in July, is reported to be about 30 days. The pouch area is protected by only slightly-developed skin folds on either side.

JERBOA MARSUPIAL MOUSE (*Antechinomys spenceri*)

This extremely elegant little marsupial inhabits the arid parts of Australia, mainly in sandy country. It is found over a large area of the interior of Western Australia and the southern parts of Northern Territory, as well as in the north of South Australia and the south-west of Queensland.

Once widely thought to be a bipedal jumping animal, similar to the desert-living jumping rodents which are found in identical localities in Australia, it has recently been shown that this jerboa marsupial mouse bounds rapidly from hind legs to fore-legs. The fore-legs as well as the hind legs are elongated, and the tail, which is very long, has a conspicuous tuft of dark brown hairs at the tip.

The diet consists of insects, spiders and centipedes. Very little is known about the breeding habits, but litters of up to 6 young have been recorded.

WHITE-FOOTED MARSUPIAL MOUSE (*Sminthopsis leucopus*)

This species is found in Tasmania and parts of the south-eastern mainland. The animal illustrated is from Tasmania. It has the general appearance of a true rat but is distinguished by the sharp-pointed snout, white feet, dark greyish-brown hair on the back and sides of the body, and white under-parts.

As these small marsupials are rarely seen, very little is known about their distribution, numbers and habits. In Tasmania they are said to be active climbers and are largely insect-eaters. A bark nest containing juveniles has been found about 45 feet up in the side of a gum-tree. It is also thought that they nest in the tops of tree ferns.

Native Cats

The native cats are all medium-sized members of the group of marsupials with many front, or incisor, teeth. Although they resemble the mongooses of other countries, their nearest relatives are the marsupial tiger cat, marsupial mice, Tasmanian devil and Tasmanian tiger. All the native cats are slender-bodied and graceful animals with white spots distributed over the body but not on the tail; the latter feature alone distinguishes them from the larger tiger cat.

EASTERN NATIVE CAT (*Dasyurus viverrinus*)

The eastern native cat was formerly distributed in the coastal forests of New South Wales, and in Victoria east of Melbourne. It has been found in the south-east of South Australia but now appears to be extinct or extremely rare in this State. It is also found in Tasmania, where it is fairly common. It is interesting to note that in recent years small colonies have been reported close to Sydney, Melbourne and Hobart.

The head and body together are about 18 inches long, and the tail about 12 inches. Grey and black colour phases, both with white spots, may occur in the same litter, irrespective of sex. Insects form a large part of the eastern native cat's diet, but it also preys upon small vertebrates.

The breeding season is in the late autumn or winter, and litters of up to 8 young are born after a short gestation period of up to 14 days. In this marsupial there is sometimes a lavish over-production of young. There is one report of 18 young being found in the pouch just after the birth. Those young which do not gain a teat must perish. There are 8 teats arranged in 2 rows of 4 on each side of a shallow pouch. The new-born young, only 7 mm. ($\frac{1}{4}$-inch) in length, have well-developed fore-limbs with deciduous claws, which are used to grip the mother's hair on the journey to the pouch. The young open their eyes at $2\frac{1}{2}$ months and they are capable of an independent existence when approximately $4\frac{1}{2}$ months old.

NORTHERN NATIVE CAT (*Satanellus hallucatus*)

The northern native cat is smaller than the other native cats and it is largely confined to the tropics. It is widespread in northern coastal districts of Western Australia and the Northern Territory, and in the north and central parts of eastern Queensland. It lives mainly in hollow logs or rock outcrops in open woodland and desert grassland. The tail is shorter than in the western native cat but it is also black at the tip.

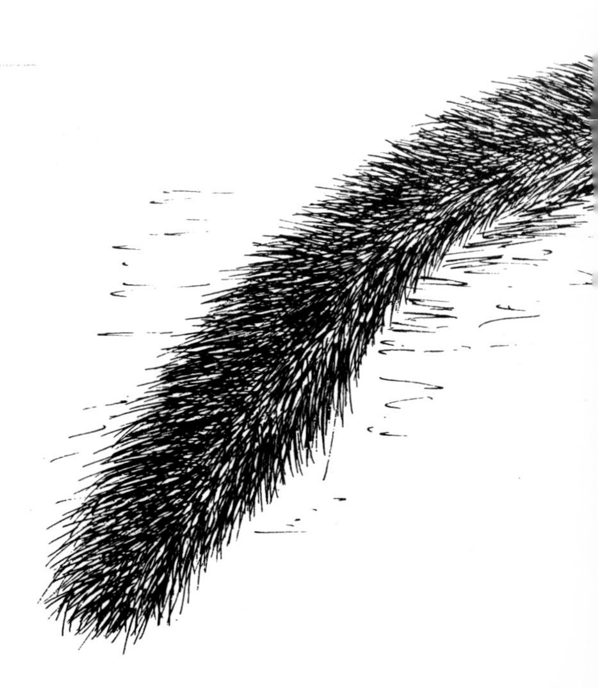

WESTERN NATIVE CAT (*Dasyurinus geoffroyi*)

The western native cat is still fairly common in the south-west of Western Australia but it now appears to be extinct in other areas. It was formerly distributed sparsely over a large part of the southern half of the continent, excluding the regions occupied by the eastern native cat. It is about the same size as the eastern native cat but differs in having a long tail, which is black at the end and along the greater part of the under-side, and also in having a distinct first toe.

TIGER CAT (*Dasyurops maculatus*)

The tiger cat of eastern Australia, including Tasmania, differs from the smaller native cats in that it has white spots on the tail as well as on the body. The general colour of the body is usually reddish-brown. It is the largest of the flesh-eating marsupials found on the Australian mainland; the head and body length combined may reach about $2\frac{1}{2}$ feet and the tail about 18 inches.

The tiger cat is fairly common in parts of New South Wales and southern Queensland. It is more plentiful in Tasmania than elsewhere, but is seldom seen because of its secretive habits. It lives mainly in forests and thickly wooded districts, and its excellent climbing ability enables it to feed on birds, as well as on ground-dwelling mammals up to the size of small wallabies.

The breeding season appears to be in the late autumn and winter, and up to 6 young are reared in a shallow pouch enclosing the mammary area. The young open their eyes when about 9 weeks old and are weaned round 5 months.

TASMANIAN DEVIL (*Sarcophilus harrisii*)

The devil is common in Tasmania, and is now found only in this State, although fossil remains have been discovered in various localities on the Australian mainland. Its hardy nature, both in the wild and in captivity, causes one to wonder how it became extinct on the mainland within comparatively recent geological times.

The Tasmanian devil is unlike any other marsupial; it is powerfully built, about the size of a cocker spaniel, and black in colour, except for a white band on the chest and often a white rump patch. Its closest relatives are the marsupial mice, native cats, tiger cat and Tasmanian tiger.

The devil is widely distributed in Tasmania where it feeds mainly on medium-sized mammals and birds. A feature of its feeding is that all of the prey is eaten, including the skin and bones. Although mainly a ground-dweller, it is a competent climber.

Breeding takes place in the late autumn and early winter and litters of 3 or 4 young are born after a gestation period of about 31 days. The period of pouch life is about 5 months.

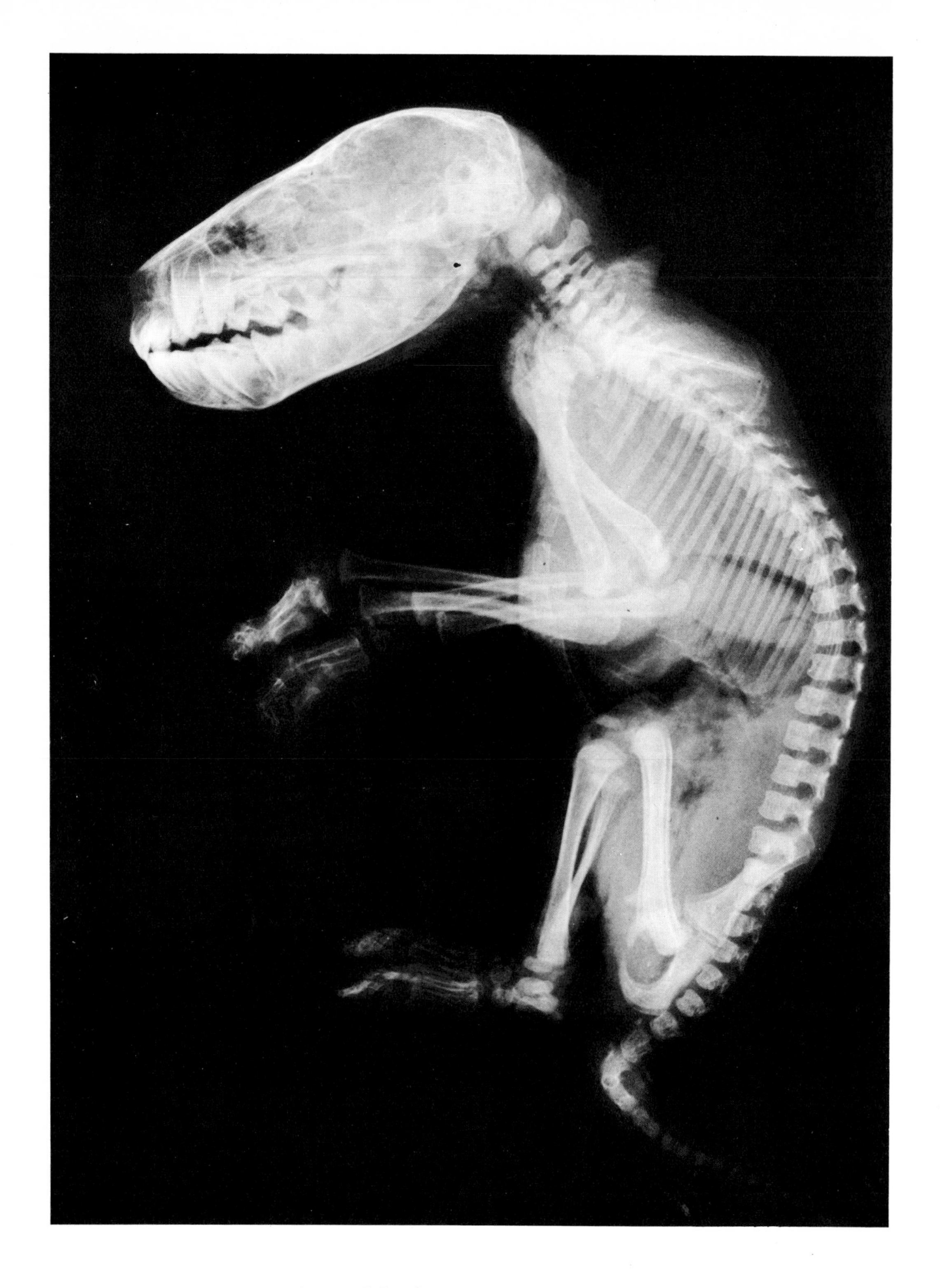

TASMANIAN DEVIL (*Sarcophilus harrisii*)

The large head, strong jaws and fearsome array of teeth of the Tasmanian devil are seen in this radiograph of an advanced pouch young. For its size, it has an excellent set of teeth.

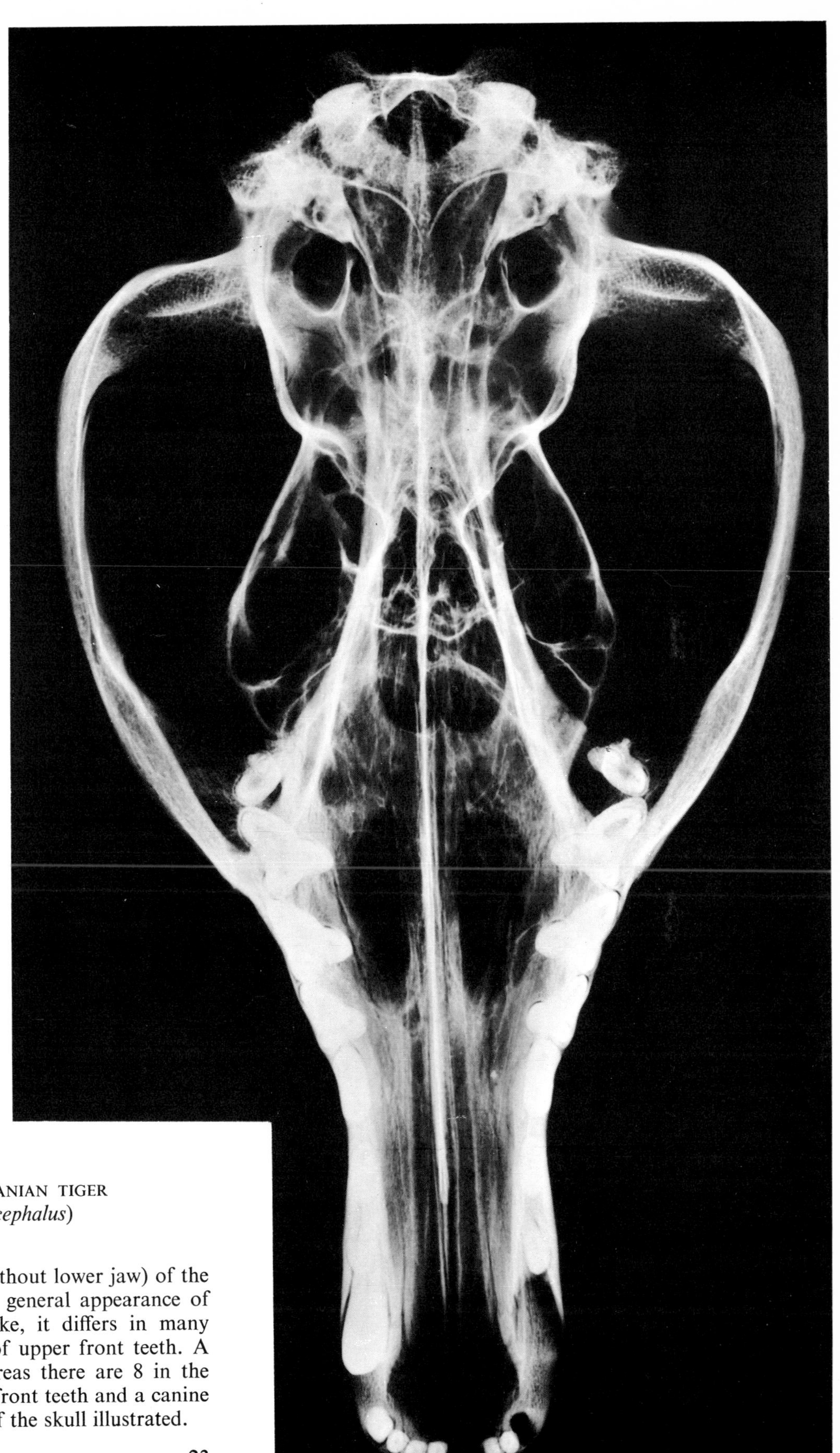

THYLACINE OR TASMANIAN TIGER
(*Thylacinus cynocephalus*)

A radiograph of the skull (without lower jaw) of the Tasmanian tiger. Although the general appearance of the skull is remarkably dog-like, it differs in many features, such as the number of upper front teeth. A dog has 6 of these teeth, whereas there are 8 in the Tasmanian tiger. Two of these front teeth and a canine tooth are missing on one side of the skull illustrated.

THYLACINE OR TASMANIAN TIGER
(*Thylacinus cynocephalus*)

This marsupial, now found only in Tasmania, once ranged widely on the Australian mainland. In addition, fossil remains have recently been found in New Guinea. It is the largest living flesh-eating marsupial known, being about 5 feet in overall length, of which the tail makes up 1¾ feet. It is dog-like in appearance, with about 16 to 18 distinctive dark-brown bars on the back, rump, and base of the tail. The general coat colour is tawny yellow-brown.

The closest relatives of the Tasmanian tiger are the marsupial mice, native cats, tiger cat, and Tasmanian devil. This tiger belongs to the family of marsupials that is characterized by having 8 incisor (front) teeth in the upper jaw, and a normal hind foot of 4 or 5 toes.

The Tasmanian tiger is usually a solitary animal, although pairs and family groups of 4 or 5 have been seen hunting together. It is mainly nocturnal, although it has been seen tracking a wallaby in daylight. Its natural food includes other marsupials, rodents, birds, and possibly even echidnas.

Once common in Tasmania, the "tiger" was very rare by 1914, and has remained so ever since. The last specimen was collected more than 30 years ago, but recent reports indicate that it is not yet extinct. In the early days of settlement of Tasmania, these animals were destroyed because they took heavy toll of the sheep and poultry.

Very little information is available on the habits and life history of this marsupial. It is thought that births usually take place in the summer, and the litter size is usually 3 or 4 young. The period of pouch life is probably about 4 months, although the young continue to suckle for some time afterwards.

NUMBAT OR BANDED ANT-EATER
(*Myrmecobius fasciatus*)

The numbat, found only in certain districts of South and Western Australia, is one of the least-known though most remarkable of the marsupials. Its size is similar to that of a large rat or squirrel, the head and body being about 9½ inches long and the tail about 7 inches long. It is a very attractive marsupial; the general colour above is greyish-brown to reddish-brown, and there are several prominent white bars across the back and rump. There is a dark stripe through the eye, which has a whitish stripe above. The tail hair is long, and the tail has a bushy appearance when the hair is erect.

In south-western Australia, the numbat lives in shrub woodland in which the majority of trees are eucalypts. The heartwood of these trees is eaten out by termites or white ants. The woodland floor is strewn with fallen hollow limbs and logs with which the animal is associated and runs to when disturbed. It feeds largely on termites, and to a lesser extent on true ants, gathering them with a long worm-like tongue which can be protruded several inches. The teeth are remarkable on account of their great number—50 to 52, the largest number found in any marsupial. The nearest relatives of the numbat are thought to be the native and tiger cats.

Numbats are unlike most small mammals in that they are active during the daytime only. In general, they are solitary animals except when the young are about. Most of the young are born from January to March. The litter size is usually 4 young, and they are carried or nursed by the mother through the winter. Although the typical marsupial pouch is absent, the young are securely held by the teats, which swell in the mouth, as in other marsupials. The young also cling by their fore-feet to the long hair of the mother's belly.

Although the numbat's range in south-western Australia has decreased considerably since European occupation, colonies are known in widely-scattered places and, at the present time, the numbat is in no danger of extinction.

LONG-NOSED BANDICOOT (*Perameles nasuta*)

This bandicoot, found only in eastern Australia from north Queensland to Victoria, is common near Sydney. The conical holes dug by the fore-feet of bandicoots in their search for food are a common feature of some gardens. Although these diggings may be disturbing to the gardener, the bandicoots are probably assisting considerably in the control of mice, slugs, snails and other destructive pests. In captivity, these bandicoots readily accept minced meat, earthworms and mice, in preference to vegetable matter.

Bandicoots

The bandicoots are among the most interesting of the marsupials, and are unique to the Australian region. They have anatomical features that link them with the two major groups of marsupials. Their dentition is like the insect- and flesh-eating families, yet they possess certain peculiarities of the hind foot, seen in the herbivorous kangaroos, wallabies and Australian possums. The fourth toe is enlarged, and the second and third toes are bound together, so that they appear as one, only the top joints and claws being free. One of the functions of these curious combined toes is that of a comb for freeing the hair from dirt and parasites. The fore-foot of a bandicoot, although similar to that of a kangaroo, usually has the first and fifth toes small and clawless, and the remaining three equally developed; in kangaroos all the toes are clawed.

The popular name "bandicoot" was originally applied to some large rats which are found over much of southern Asia. It is derived from the Telugu language, spoken in southern India, and means "pig-rat".

There are a large number of species of marsupial bandicoots and they range in size from a rat to a rabbit. Though an elongated snout is characteristic of all bandicoots, the head is stouter and the muzzle correspondingly shorter in the short-nosed species. The ears are short and rounded in the short-nosed bandicoots, more pointed in the long-nosed bandicoots, and greatly elongated in the rabbit-eared and pig-footed bandicoots. The great interest attached to the pig-footed bandicoot (Chaeropus ecaudatus) *lies in the modification of the feet; the fore-foot has only two functional toes, and the hind foot only one.*

In general, bandicoots are disappearing over the whole of continental Australia. For example, the extraordinary pig-footed species, which once had an extremely wide distribution, has apparently disappeared from all former areas, and it now appears to be one of the unique marsupials threatened with ultimate extinction, if it is not already extinct.

Information on various aspects of the natural history of all but a few bandicoots is sadly lacking. In view of the unique zoological position occupied by these marsupials and the comparative rarity of many species, it is hoped that they will receive wider public interest, and that the species which remain will not be added to the growing list of extinct mammals.

LONG-NOSED BANDICOOT (*Perameles nasuta*)

Bandicoots are typical marsupials in that the young are born at a very early stage of development, and are reared within a pouch. This pouch, which opens downwards and backwards, contains 8 teats arranged in 2 curved rows of four. This is the typical arrangement of the teats in the bandicoot family. Each teat is associated with a separate milk gland.

The 3 young shown in this picture are about 4 days old. Eight is the maximum number of young that can be accommodated in the pouch, but litters greater than 5 have not been reported in this species. Litters of 2 or 3 young appear to be the most common. New-born specimens are about 13 mm. ($\frac{1}{2}$-inch) long and weigh about $\frac{1}{4}$-gramme (less than $\frac{1}{100}$-oz.). The mother usually weighs about 900 grammes, which is about 3,600 times heavier than the new-born baby. The gestation period, or the period of development before birth, is about 12 days. At birth, the young resemble other marsupials in that they are provided with strongly-developed fore-limbs, and the fore-feet are equipped with well-developed claws. These special claws are only temporary in the bandicoots studied but, no doubt, they help the new-born to take hold of the mother's hair on its way to the pouch.

The new-born bandicoot sucks a teat into its mouth and remains firmly attached during most of its pouch life. The sucked teats enlarge and elongate during this period; they help to hold the young within the pouch as well as acting as milk ducts. At no time is there any union between the teat and the young, which can always be removed by pulling gently. The lips of the young are fused at the sides until they are about 5 weeks old, when they release the teats for the first time.

LONG-NOSED BANDICOOT (*Perameles nasuta*)

Bandicoots grow more rapidly than any of the other marsupials that have been studied. At 6 or 7 weeks after birth they are covered with short hair and the eyes are open. This drawing shows a juvenile which ventured out of the pouch for the first time when about 7½ weeks old. At this stage, the young is unsteady on its feet. Females may start breeding when only half-grown at about 4 months of age, and males may be sexually mature when 5 months old. Near Sydney, the long-nosed bandicoot breeds all the year round. The number of litters a year is not yet known, but it is known that some animals become pregnant while still suckling a litter.

LONG-NOSED BANDICOOT (*Perameles nasuta*)

A bandicoot about 8 weeks old entering its mother's pouch, which increases in size as the young grow. When the young are about 9 to 10 weeks old they are too large to return to the pouch, but they may continue to suckle for another one to two weeks. In females carrying young, the lining of the pouch is moist and a characteristic yellow waxy secretion usually appears in the pouch and round its opening.

BARRED BANDICOOT (*Perameles gunnii*)

A barred rump is characteristic of most members of the genus *Perameles*, which are all long-nosed bandicoots. The species illustrated, common in Tasmania, is also found in southern Victoria. It is smaller and more slenderly built than *Perameles nasuta*, the common long-nosed bandicoot of eastern Australia.

In Tasmania, the barred bandicoot mainly occurs in open paddock areas. During the day it occupies a nest in tufts of grass or in dense vegetation, and at night its main activity is foraging and feeding. In common with some other bandicoots, this barred species is mainly insectivorous. Earthworms, large insect larvae, and adult beetles are the main foods taken. Ripe berries are taken when available.

Young leave the pouch at 7 weeks of age, and they are weaned when about 2 months old. About one to two weeks later they are independent of their mother. Females are sexually mature round 3 months of age, and males between 4 and 5 months. Three or four litters are born during the breeding season, which lasts from May to February. The number of young in each litter is between 1 and 4, with 2 or 3 young being the most common.

LITTLE BARRED BANDICOOT (*Perameles bougainvillei*)

This small bandicoot, which has ill-defined bars on the rump, now appears to be confined to Bernier and Dorre islands at the entrance to Shark Bay on the west coast of Western Australia. The first account of this species, published in 1824, refers to a specimen collected by a French expedition on the mainland of Shark Bay. The last mainland specimen received by the Western Australian Museum was collected in this region in 1909. At the present time, this bandicoot is extremely common on both islands and, at night, it is found among the sandhills. Pouch young have been collected in July, but very little is known about the length of the breeding season.

SHORT-NOSED BANDICOOT (*Isoodon obesulus*)

The general form of this bandicoot is stout, and the outer coat is composed of coarse stiff hairs. Adult specimens are about 14 inches long. It is the most widely distributed of all bandicoots, and it is common in many places, such as Tasmania, Victoria and the south-west of Western Australia.

The nest, usually constructed in dense vegetation, has no permanent hole, for short-nosed bandicoots burrow in and out at any aspect. They are not frequently seen, for they hide away during the day. They feed at night and make numerous holes, sometimes quite deep, in their search for earthworms, insects and insect larvae. They occasionally feed on ripe berries.

In Tasmania this bandicoot can produce at least 2 litters, probably 3 in a breeding season, which lasts from May to February. A new litter may be born as soon as the old one is weaned, when about 2 months old. The number of young in each litter is between 1 and 5, usually 2 or 3.

BILBY OR RABBIT-EARED BANDICOOT (*Thylacomys lagotis*)

This is the largest of the 3 species of rabbit-eared bandicoots or bilbies. They are all delightful, medium-sized marsupials with bluish-grey fur, often with a pinkish tinge, and with long ears. Rabbit-eared bandicoots are also unique; they are the only bandicoots that live in burrows.

The specimen illustrated is from Western Australia.

The range of this species has decreased considerably since European occupation, and they are now found only in the drier parts of Western Australia, and central Australia near the junction of Queensland and the Northern Territory. Formerly they were found in central and western New South Wales, north-west Victoria and central and northern South Australia. In the Northern Territory they are sparsely distributed over a wide area in mulga and spinifex country, and their chief food has been found to be termites. In the absence of free water, which occurs only after rains, the rabbit-eared bandicoot presumably obtains sufficient water from this food. It feeds at night and lives in a burrow from 3 to 6 feet deep during the day, thus escaping the intense solar radiation.

It would appear that the rabbit-eared bandicoots are disappearing all over Australia. At the present time, not enough is known about how these marsupials live to say why they are apparently extinct in some areas and disappearing in others.

HAIRY-NOSED WOMBAT (*Lasiorhinus latifrons*)

The soft, silky hair, long ears, and hairy snout, distinguish this species from other wombats. It occurs on the open plains of South Australia, from the Murray River west across the Nullarbor Plain to the border of Western Australia, and in inland regions of south-eastern Queensland. In limestone country on the west bank of the Murray River at Blanchetown, South Australia, it lives in extensive communal warrens, and the entrances are often situated below a limestone ledge at the bottom of a large crater.

Although these wombats feed at night, and their herbivorous diet is similar to that of the common wombat, they are often seen near the burrow entrance during the day. The breeding season appears to be in the early summer in the Murray River area of South Australia, and later in the summer in the more arid Nullarbor Plain area.

COMMON WOMBAT (*Vombatus hirsutus*)

This thick-set, marmot-like marsupial is found mainly in hilly or mountainous parts of eastern New South Wales and southern Victoria, and in low-lying districts of the south-eastern parts of South Australia. It grows to about 3½ feet in total length and weighs up to 80 lb. It has short ears, a bare snout and coarse hair that is dark brown to black. The tail is reduced to a mere rudiment.

At night this wombat feeds on grasses, roots and other vegetable matter, and during the day it lives in a large burrow which it digs with its powerful fore-claws. The burrow entrance, about 18 inches in diameter, is usually situated at the base of a tree or rock. A burrow at least 40 feet long and descending to 6 feet below the surface of the ground has been reported. In some of the comparatively inaccessible and unused parts of South Australia there are huge warrens with cave-like entrances, known to have been occupied for more than a century.

The pouch opens backwards, the reverse of that in kangaroos, and a single baby is born in the autumn or winter.

TASMANIAN WOMBAT (*Vombatus ursinus*)

Wombats are burrowing, herbivorous marsupials, with specialized gnawing teeth which resemble the front teeth (incisors) of beavers and other rodents in that they grow continuously from persistent pulps as the tips are worn away. Wombats are the only marsupials in which all the teeth are of this type. The radiograph shows the strongly-developed teeth, as well as the skeleton, in an advanced pouch young. The majority of marsupials have a different number of front teeth in the upper and lower jaws, but in the wombats, these teeth are reduced to a single pair in each jaw. An interesting feature of this wombat and the common wombat (*Vombatus hirsutus*) is that there are 15 pairs of ribs; in the hairy-nosed wombats, and most other marsupials, there are only 13 pairs.

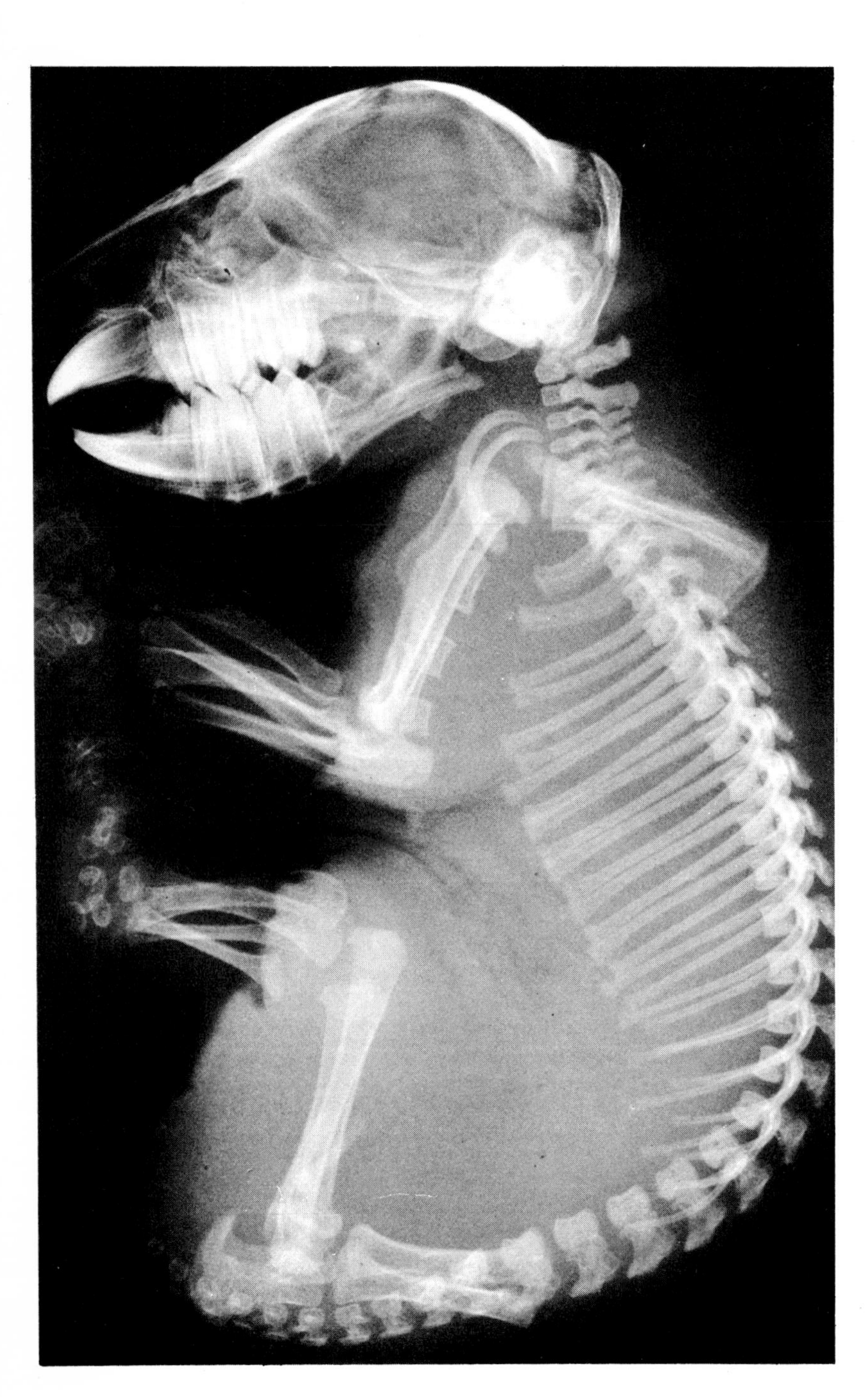

Possums

Many different kinds of possums, or phalangers, are found in the Australian region and they are among the most attractive of the marsupials. They range in weight from a few ounces to several pounds and they include the honey and pygmy possums, gliding possums, ring-tailed and brush-tailed possums, and cuscuses.

Possums are all adapted to a tree-dwelling existence and most are vegetarian in diet. Both pairs of limbs are well developed for grasping and climbing; the hind foot has a thumb-like first toe for gripping branches securely. Many possums also have a tail which can be wrapped round a branch for added safety. The second and third toes of the hind foot are joined together, except for the top joints, a peculiarity which is also seen in the bandicoots and members of the kangaroo family.

Although no member of the possum family has become extinct since European occupation, several species are uncommon, and they are in danger of extermination unless a special effort is made on their behalf.

DORMOUSE OR PYGMY POSSUM (*Cercartetus nanus*)

This delightful mouse-like possum, also called a "dormouse" possum, inhabits Tasmania and the coastal regions of south-eastern Australia. The possum illustrated is from Tasmania. Cavities in trees are used as shelters, and the animal is sometimes found at the end of a tunnel excavated in the decaying wood in the stump of a dead tree. The entrance to the burrow is closed with loosely-packed particles of rotten wood.

The soft hair is a dull grey colour above, with the under-parts and feet almost white. The eyes are large and prominent, each being surrounded by a dark area.

It is generally claimed that the pygmy possum is strictly nocturnal, but this is not so with specimens kept in captivity. Although these possums usually remain in a sleeping box until dusk before coming out to feed, there are occasions when they come out even at midday or in the afternoon, especially if the sky is clouded and the light dull. Activity and dormancy alternate throughout the year, the longest period of dormancy recorded in captivity being 12 days. Captive specimens show a marked preference for insects, but spiders, dead scorpions, and even small lizards are readily accepted.

HONEY POSSUM (*Tarsipes spenserae*)

The little honey possum of the south-west of Western Australia is one of the very specialized marsupials. It grows to about the size of a common house mouse, the head and body measuring about 3 inches and the tail 4 inches.

Among the distinguishing features of this small animal are the very long snout and long tongue, specially adapted for inserting into flowers and feeding on nectar, upon which it chiefly subsists. The bottle-brush appears to be a favourite source of this food.

Another distinguishing feature of the honey possum is its coloration, especially the three dark stripes along the back. The central stripe, almost black, extends from the head to the base of the tail, while the two outer ones are fainter and do not reach the tail. In the hind foot, the honey possum has the second and third toes greatly reduced, and almost completely enclosed in a common sheath, while the fourth toe is greatly enlarged and, like the fifth, is provided with a nail instead of a claw, as in the monkeys.

SUGAR GLIDER (*Petaurus breviceps*)

Some possums have developed a parachute-like membrane between the fore-legs and hind legs which enables them to glide through the air from one tree to another. Although they are often called "flying" possums, they cannot fly like birds or bats. The largest of the gliding possums—the greater glider (*Schoinobates volans*)—is the size of a cat, the head and body being about 17 inches long and the tail about 20 inches long. The smallest—the pygmy or feather-tail glider (*Acrobates pygmaeus*)—is about the size of a mouse; it has a narrow gliding membrane along the flanks between the fore-legs and hind legs, and the feather-like tail has a row of stiff hairs on each side.

The very attractive sugar glider is intermediate in size, and the one illustrated is from Tasmania. It is widely distributed in the scrub and forests of eastern Australia, from Cape York to Victoria and eastern South Australia, and is also found in the northern part of the Northern Territory. It is thought that the early settlers introduced it into Tasmania, where it is now widespread.

The sugar glider is readily distinguished by its beautiful, soft, dove-grey fur and by the well-developed gliding membrane running from wrist to ankle on either side of the body. The tail is long and bushy and there is a dark stripe on top of the head and on the centre of the back. The underside of the body and gliding membrane is greyish-white. The body measures about 7 to 8 inches from nose to tail-base.

The sugar glider feeds at night on insects, fruits, buds and blossoms. It makes a nest in a tree-hollow, and family groups often inhabit the same nest. Breeding is restricted to the second half of the year. The litter size is usually 2, and females that give birth early sometimes produce, and rear, a second litter at the end of the breeding season.

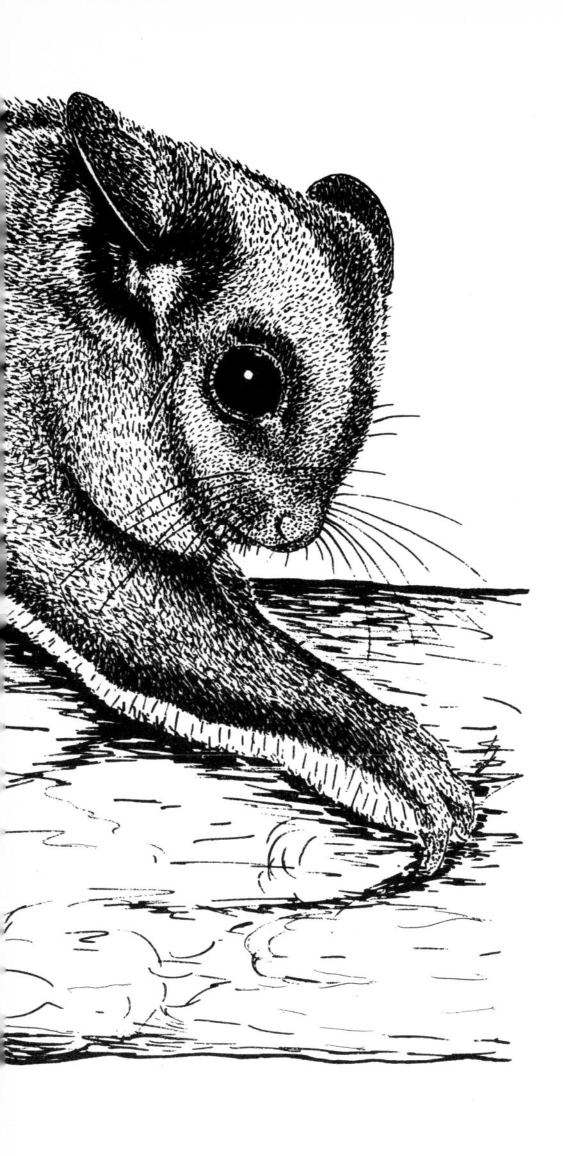

TASMANIAN RING-TAILED POSSUM
(*Pseudocheirus convolutor*)

There are many different kinds of ring-tailed possums, and they are among the most familiar of the native mammals of eastern Australia. There is also one in the south-west of Western Australia and another in the north of the Northern Territory.

The photograph shows the strongly-developed claws of the fore-foot of a juvenile pouch young of the ring-tailed possum found in Tasmania. The new-born young uses these strong claws to grasp the mother's hair on its way to the pouch.

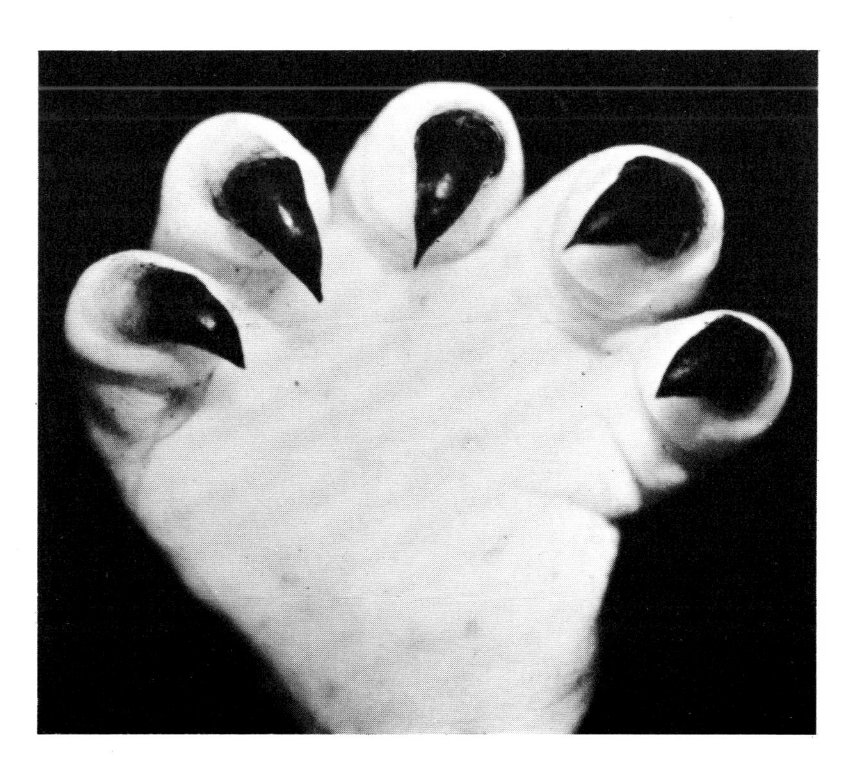

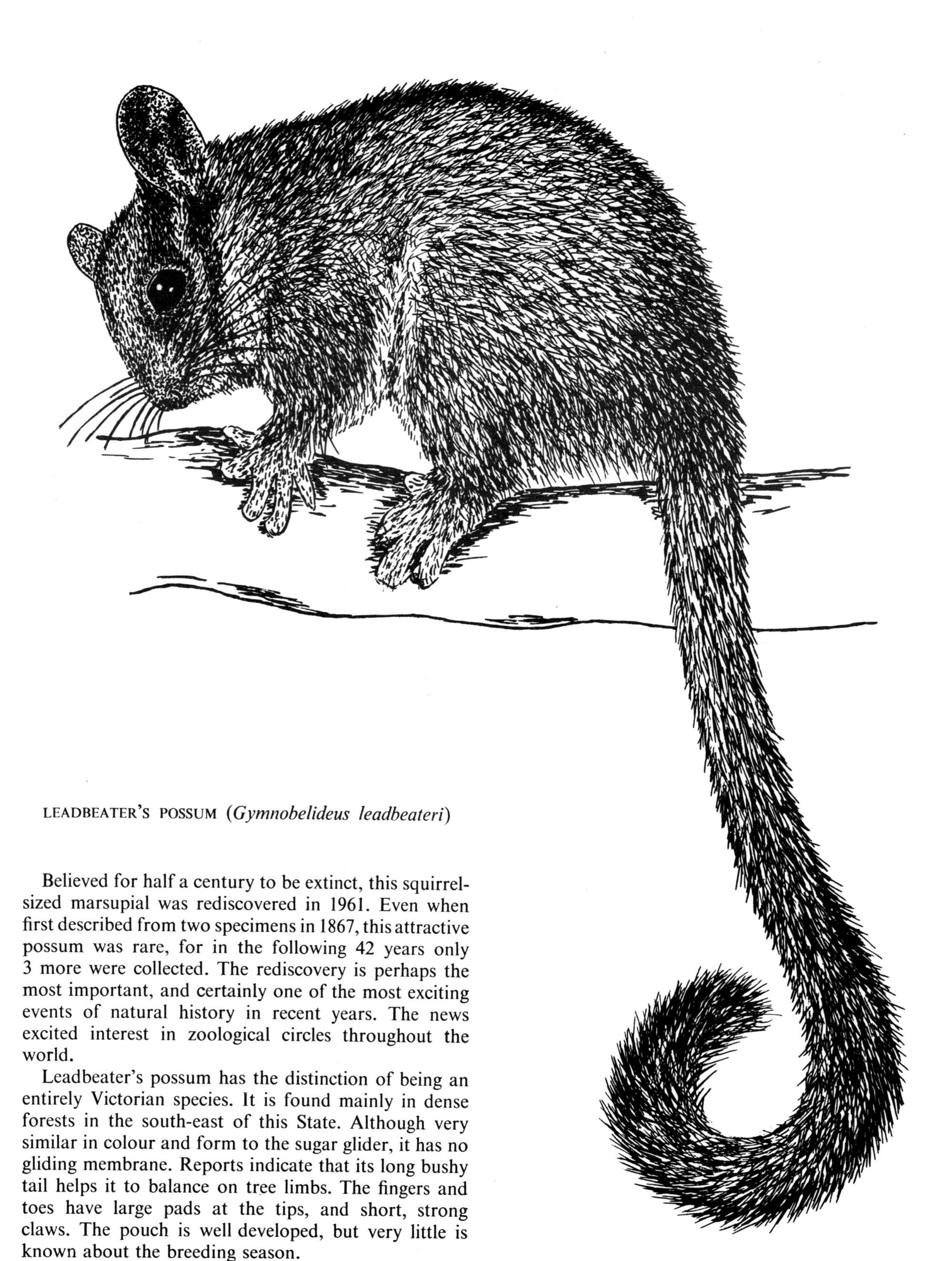

LEADBEATER'S POSSUM (*Gymnobelideus leadbeateri*)

Believed for half a century to be extinct, this squirrel-sized marsupial was rediscovered in 1961. Even when first described from two specimens in 1867, this attractive possum was rare, for in the following 42 years only 3 more were collected. The rediscovery is perhaps the most important, and certainly one of the most exciting events of natural history in recent years. The news excited interest in zoological circles throughout the world.

Leadbeater's possum has the distinction of being an entirely Victorian species. It is found mainly in dense forests in the south-east of this State. Although very similar in colour and form to the sugar glider, it has no gliding membrane. Reports indicate that its long bushy tail helps it to balance on tree limbs. The fingers and toes have large pads at the tips, and short, strong claws. The pouch is well developed, but very little is known about the breeding season.

BRUSH-TAILED POSSUM (*Trichosurus vulpecula*)

The brush-tailed possum, about the size of a domestic cat is one of the largest and commonest of the possums. This marsupial is commonly found in wooded and forested areas over much of continental Australia, Tasmania and some off-shore islands. In the semi-deserts of central Australia, it shelters in the trees that border the watercourses. In the suburbs of Sydney, Adelaide, and Perth, as well as other cities, it often shelters in the roofs of houses. Various types of dens of this possum are known, both natural and unnatural. The common natural type is a hollow eucalypt branch, more or less regardless of height above ground. Holes at the base of trees are also used. Unless disturbed, this possum is seldom seen during daylight. It feeds at night, mainly on leaves and fruits of various trees and shrubs.

The coloration is extremely variable, especially in Tasmania, where black and grey colour phases are the most common. Very large numbers have been killed for their skins. The coat is thick, soft and woolly, and a distinguishing feature is the well-haired tail, which can be wrapped round a branch when climbing. The terminal portion of the tail is naked on the underside.

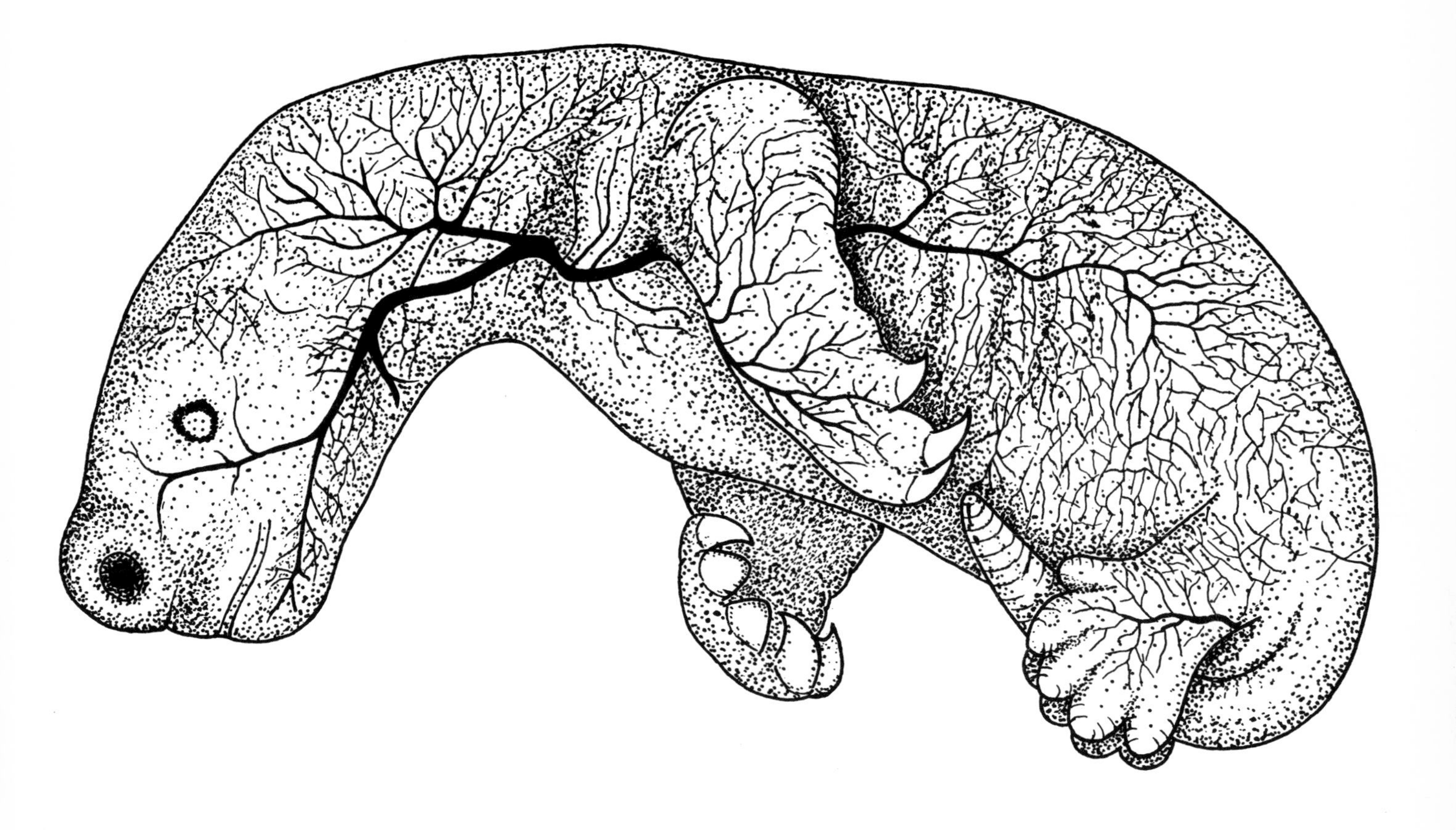

BRUSH-TAILED POSSUM (*Trichosurus vulpecula*)

This large possum has a well-developed glandular area, and distinctive brown-coloured hair on the chest. The brown coloration comes from the skin secretions, which also give the hairs a wet, oily appearance. With the approach of the breeding season, the coloration of the chest becomes more conspicuous, particularly in the male. Observations on both wild and captive animals have revealed that the chest is rubbed against trees and other objects, suggesting that it has an important function in marking territories. It is also very probable that the chest patch attracts the other sex by its colour and by the odour of its copious secretion. The odour, and probably the stain, from the glands of the mother may assist the young to find its parent after it has left the pouch.

The new-born young of the brush-tailed possum, shown in this drawing, is only about 13 mm. (½-inch) long and weighs ⅕-gramme compared with the mother's weight of about 2,000 grammes. This means that the mother is about 10,000 times heavier than the new-born young. The gestation period is about 17½ days.

The living new-born is semi-transparent and pinkish in colour, with a conspicuous network of blood vessels visible through the skin. The fore-limbs are strongly developed, and the fore-feet have well-developed, sharp-pointed claws turned inwards towards the palm. As the fore-limbs alone are used in climbing into the pouch, these claws appear to be important structures that aid the young to grip the mother's fur. These claws are not shed during pouch life as are those of bandicoots, native cats, and some other marsupials.

BRUSH-TAILED POSSUM (*Trichosurus vulpecula*)

The brush-tailed possum is one of the best known of the tree-climbing marsupials. The one shown in this drawing is about 4½ months old. Although it is now too large to be accommodated in the mother's pouch, it continues to suckle by putting its head in the pouch. Weaning is at about 6 months, and sexual maturity is reached round 12 to 15 months. The main breeding season is in the autumn, although winter and spring births are not uncommon.

BRUSH-TAILED POSSUM (*Trichosurus vulpecula*)

The brush-tailed possum is usually about 3½ months old when the eyes open, and it ventures out of the pouch soon afterwards. This attractive possum is 4 months old.

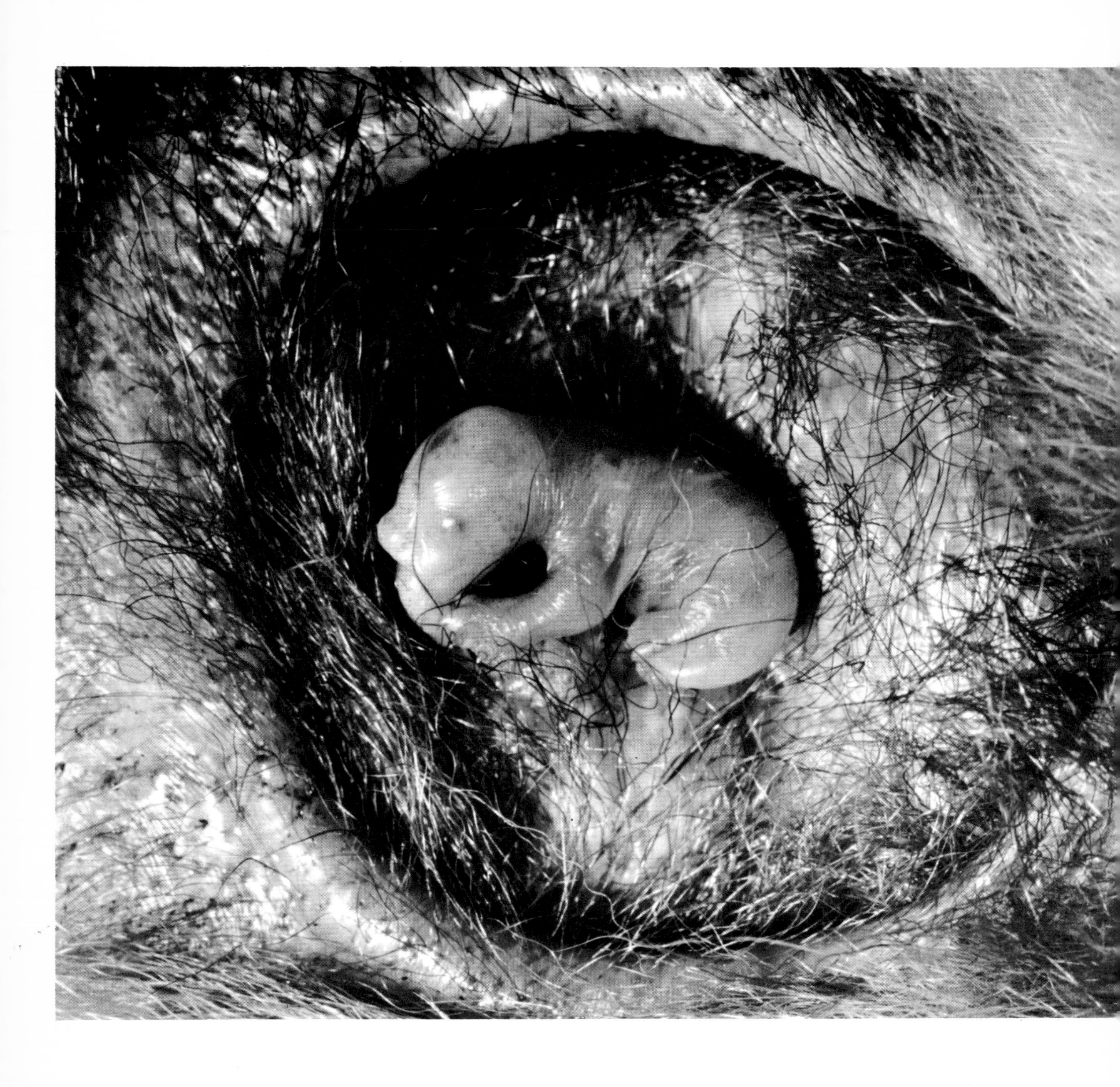

BRUSH-TAILED POSSUM (*Trichosurus vulpecula*)

A baby possum, about 5 days old, within its mother's pouch. The mouth of the pouch has been opened in order to take the photograph. The young remains permanently attached to one of two teats for several months. Usually only one young is born at a time and it is carried in the mother's pouch for 4 to 5 months.

Kangaroos

In addition to the well-known large kangaroos and wallabies, there are many other members of the kangaroo family. Less known are the various rat-kangaroos, hare-wallabies, rock-wallabies and tree-kangaroos. All of these marsupials, except the tree-kangaroos, are adapted to living on the ground, and they are able to progress rapidly by jumping with their powerful hind limbs. The hind foot, with its very large fourth toe, forms the main support for the weight of the body. The tail is usually long and powerful, and aids in supporting the body. The pouch is well developed, with the opening directed forwards. There are 4 teats, but only one young is born at a time.

Some members of the kangaroo family have developed an interesting process of digestion similar to that seen in sheep, cattle and other true ruminants. The stomach is large and folded, and digestion is carried out mainly by enormous numbers of bacteria and protozoa.

The musk rat-kangaroo (Hypsiprymnodon moschatus) *of north-east coastal Queensland is the smallest and, in some respects, the most peculiar of the kangaroo family. It may be distinguished from other members of this family by the presence of a first toe on the hind foot. This toe is clawless, as in the possums, but is only semi-opposable to the other toes.*

At least 5 of the 6 marsupial species known to have become extinct since European occupation are members of the kangaroo family. There is evidence that at least 2 of these, both rat-kangaroos, were on the way out before the arrival of the white man, because of long-term environmental changes, and presumably such influences are still at work.

POTOROO OR LONG-NOSED RAT-KANGAROO
(*Potorous tridactylus*)

The potoroo is one of the small kangaroo-like marsupials. Sexually mature females range in weight from 1½ to 3 pounds and males weigh round 3 pounds when fully adult. This marsupial, now rare on the Australian mainland, is still common in many parts of Tasmania, and appears to be in no danger of extinction. On the mainland it has been recorded from south-eastern Queensland, eastern New South Wales, Victoria and South Australia. In Tasmania, the potoroo usually inhabits regions of thick scrub or forest, and it feeds at night mainly on herbage and roots. It oftens digs small holes in the ground like those made by bandicoots.

Observations on both captive and wild populations in Tasmania suggest the existence of two breeding seasons, one in late winter and early spring, the other in the summer. The gestation period is about 38 days and the newly-born offspring, only ¾-in. long, takes about 10 minutes to crawl into the pouch. The young remains permanently attached to a teat for about 2 months and it continues to suckle until it is at least 4 months old. The potoroo resembles most other members of the kangaroo family in that it mates soon after giving birth, and a dormant embryo is then held in the uterus. The period of delayed pregnancy can be as long as 4½ months.

BANDED HARE-WALLABY (*Lagostrophus fasciatus*)

This small, timid wallaby is restricted to Western Australia, where it is now found on several islands (Bernier, Dorre and Dirk Hartogs) near Shark Bay. It was once fairly widespread in the south-west of Western Australia, and also was known as a living animal in South Australia, but it now appears to be extinct in both of these areas. Both Bernier and Dorre islands possess large and stable populations, and it is the most abundant mammal. The one illustrated is from this locality.

Although this wallaby was one of the earliest of the Australian marsupials to be made known to Europeans, more than 200 years ago, the first scientific description was not written until 1807. The banding on the rump, from which it gets its name, is well marked in juveniles, but may not be obvious in old animals.

There is little indication of a breeding season, since pouch young of all ages have been obtained in expeditions to the islands from February to August. The litter size is one.

YELLOW-FOOTED ROCK-WALLABY (*Petrogale xanthopus*)

This handsome wallaby is one of the most brightly coloured members of the kangaroo family; it is distinguished from all other wallabies by the alternate rings of brown and yellow on the tail, and by the yellow colour on the backs of its ears. The bright yellow coloration of the fore-legs and hind legs is also a striking feature. The tail is long and not thickened at the base as in large kangaroos.

Found now only in rocky country in eastern South Australia, it formerly occurred in western New South Wales and south-western Queensland, but has almost disappeared from many of its old haunts.

SPECTACLED HARE-WALLABY
(*Lagorchestes conspicillatus*)

The spectacled hare-wallaby is found mainly in the tropics. It is widely distributed on the mainland—northern Western Australia, Northern Territory and coastal Queensland. The one illustrated is from Barrow Island, off the north-west coast of Western Australia.

The species name refers to the reddish patches encircling the eyes, which give a spectacled appearance. In central Australia it is apparently a solitary-living and nocturnal animal. The first of this species of hare-wallaby were collected on Barrow Island in 1840, and it was reported to be still plentiful in 1958.

ROTHSCHILD'S ROCK-WALLABY (*Petrogale rothschildi*)

This wallaby inhabits a very limited hot and arid area of north-western Australia, and is distinguished from the widely distributed Western rock-wallaby (*Petrogale lateralis*) by its dark head and uniformly dark ears, the absence of a dark neck-stripe and whitish flank-patch, and by its shorter and thinner hair.

LUMHOLTZ'S TREE-KANGAROO (*Dendrolagus lumholtzi*)

The tree-kangaroos in Australia are represented by only two species (*Dendrolagus lumholtzi* and *Dendrolagus bennettianus*), and they are restricted to mountainous rain-forests in north-eastern Queensland. It is thought that the tree-kangaroos entered Australia from New Guinea, where they are found throughout the island.

In the process of returning to a tree-climbing existence the tree-kangaroos have changed considerably from ground-dwelling kangaroos. The fore-legs have become almost as long as the hind legs and the fore-paws are large and powerfully clawed. The hind feet have shortened and broadened. By using both sets of limbs tree-kangaroos can climb trees quite easily. The tail, which is long and of uniform diameter throughout, acts as a balancing organ; it is not used for gripping branches, but is often used to brace the animal when climbing.

Lumholtz's tree-kangaroo is distinguished from the other Australian species by the pale band across the forehead.

TASMANIAN WALLABY OR PADEMELON

(*Thylogale billardieri*)

This is the smaller of the two wallabies found in Tasmania. It is distinguished from Bennett's wallaby (the other Tasmanian species) by its smaller size, stout form and short ears. It is an inhabitant of the scrub, and spends most of its time in thick bush, whereas Bennett's wallaby may be found in fairly open country.

The species illustrated is also called the red-bellied wallaby, but its colour varies considerably. The most common colour is a dark reddish-brown with reddish or yellow-brown hair on the belly.

Colonies of this wallaby are widely distributed and plentiful in Tasmania, and very large numbers have been killed for their skins. It breeds throughout the year. One young is born at a time and takes about a year to reach maturity.

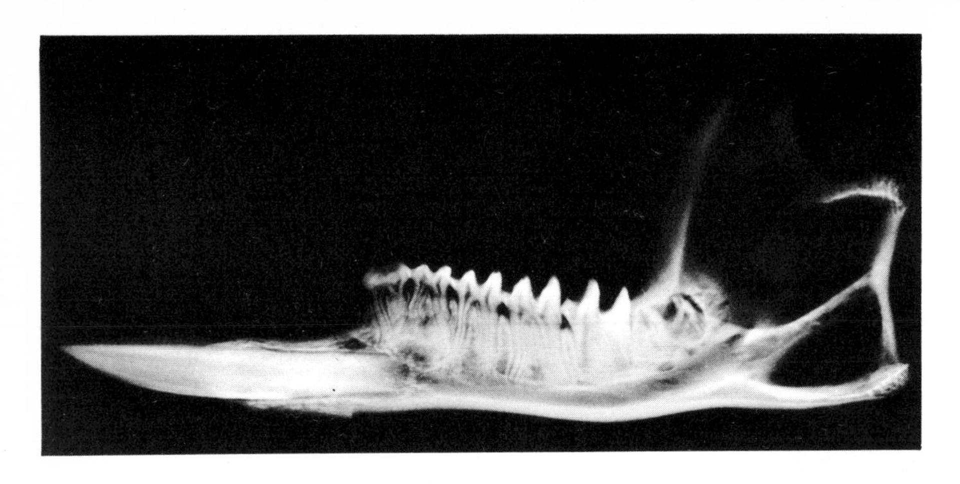

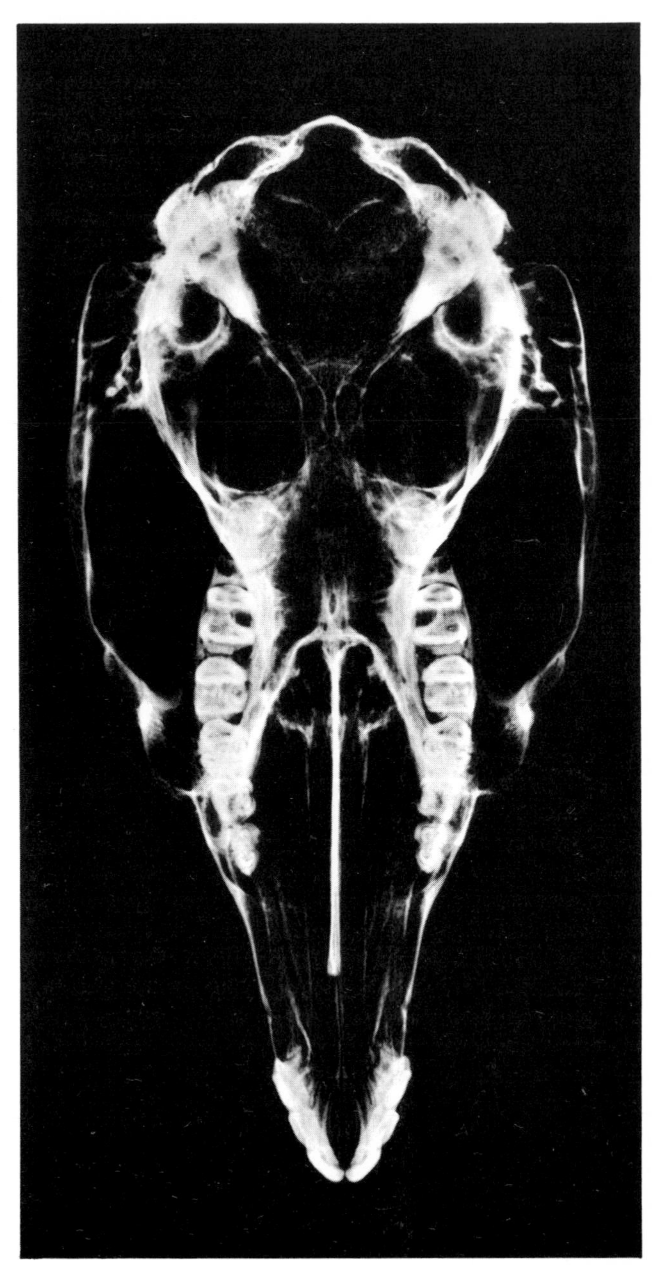

TASMANIAN WALLABY OR PADEMELON
(*Thylogale billardieri*)

Members of the kangaroo family have 3 pairs of front, or incisor, teeth in the upper jaw, and one pair in the lower. A large space separates these teeth from the cheek, or molar, teeth. The radiograph of the lower jaw shows the large root of an incisor extending back to below the roots of the front molars.

The development of the teeth in the kangaroos, particularly in the large species, is complicated by the general progression forward in the jaw of the whole row of molar teeth. In conjunction with this shift forward the hindmost molar completes its eruption, and the first and second teeth drop out and are replaced by a single tooth—the so-called "permanent" premolar.

QUOKKA OR SHORT-TAILED WALLABY
(*Setonix brachyurus*)

Once widely distributed in the south-west of Western Australia, this short-tailed wallaby is now reduced to remnant colonies on the mainland. It is still abundant on two islands, Rottnest and Bald, off Western Australia. The Rottnest colony is by far the better known, because of its accessibility to scientists in Perth, and the fact that the island is a popular holiday resort.

Quokkas are mainly nocturnal, although they may be seen moving about under the shade of trees and shrubs during the day. At night they emerge from cover to graze in the more open areas. They eat a large variety of ground vegetation, and a favourite food is a wattle which grows up to 15 feet high on Rottnest Island. In spite of their build, quokkas have been observed browsing in these trees, about 5 feet from the ground, having climbed the tree and moved far out from the trunk along the branches.

The main season of births is from February till April, although a few young are born in later months of the year. The normal gestation period is 27 days. In common with other marsupials, the new-born young of the quokka is very small, being about an inch in length and approximately 1/7000 of its mother's weight. Although the mother has 4 teats, only one young is born at a time, and it uses only one teat. It does not leave the pouch until 4 to 6 months have passed, but is still dependent upon the mother for milk, and is not weaned until 9 to 10 months old.

Approximately one day after a young is born, the female mates again. If fertilization takes place, the resulting embryo develops for only a few days and is then held in a state of suspended animation. This dormant embryo remains in the uterus, or womb, during the time the pouch is occupied by a suckling young. When this young leaves the pouch at 4 to 6 months of age, or if it is lost prematurely, the dormant embryo resumes development and is born in about 25 or 26 days. Dormant embryos in the quokka are known to be capable of completing development for periods of up to nearly 5 months. Delayed births of this type are a feature of reproduction in many kangaroos, and some of the higher mammals.

WHIPTAIL OR PRETTY-FACE WALLABY
(*Macropus parryi*)

This beautiful marsupial is distinguished from all other brush wallabies by the distinct cheek markings and by the excessively long and slender tail, equalling the combined length of the head and body. It inhabits the open woodlands of coastal Queensland and northern New South Wales. In the Dawson Valley of central coastal Queensland, it spends the greater part of its time in very open country, and is more easily approached than other wallabies. Typical of the whiptail habitats are the upland parks of the broad-leafed ironbark, a species of gum-tree, which are found in this area. This country is richly grassed with low rocky outcrops, where the whiptail makes its camps. It is rarely or never seen in the scrub. Except during the hottest weather, it may be seen feeding in the mornings and again in the afternoons. In winter it may be seen about all day. It is said to be distinctly social in habit, and parties of about a dozen animals are frequently seen lying together in the camps.

TAMMAR OR DAMA WALLABY (*Macropus eugenii*)

The tammar has the distinction of being the first known Australian marsupial. The Dutch merchant, Francisco Pelsaert, shipwrecked on the west coast of Australia in 1629, suggested that the young of this wallaby grew from a teat in the pouch, a belief that is occasionally advanced to this day. The tammar has a wide coastal range extending from Kangaroo Island, South Australia, to the south-west of Western Australia, including certain isolated islands off the coast.

The general colour of the tammars on Kangaroo Island is dark grey-brown, becoming rufous on the sides of the body and on the limbs. The drawing shows a specimen from an island off the west coast of Western Australia.

Unlike the red kangaroo, which is virtually a continuous breeder, the tammar has a non-breeding period in the spring and early summer. The gestation period is 29 days. The storage of a dormant embryo in the uterus (or womb), similar to that described in the quokka and red kangaroo, may last for up to 11 months, the longest period of delayed development known in any mammal. Delayed development of this type occurs only in females already carrying young in the pouch. The new baby is then born at the beginning of the breeding season in late summer.

GREY KANGAROO OR FORESTER (*Macropus giganteus*)

The great grey kangaroo of the forest and scrub country and the red kangaroo of the plains are the largest of all present day marsupials. Both species may stand 6 feet in height and measure 8 to 9 feet from muzzle to tail tip.

Grey kangaroos are found in regions of uniform or winter rainfall. They are distributed from north Queensland through New South Wales and Victoria to South Australia, including Kangaroo Island, and Tasmania. They are also found in the south-west of Western Australia. In Victoria, this kangaroo is the most common of the large herbivorous marsupials and, being a grazing rather than a browsing animal, sometimes competes with agricultural stock for food.

Differences in appearances are seen between grey kangaroos from different localities. In eastern Australia they vary from the long haired, silver-grey forms of the coastal forests to the shorter haired, black faced, and dark bodied forms of the dense inland scrub.

The gestation period (29 to 38 days) in the grey kangaroo is much more variable than in other marsupials. This kangaroo exhibits an interesting variation of the delayed birth mechanism found in other members of the kangaroo family. Instead of mating just after the young is born, mating may occur about 4 months later, and the fertilized embryo is held in the uterus in a dormant state during the time the pouch is occupied by a suckling young. The period of pouch life is about 10 months. After leaving the pouch the young may be suckled by the mother for at least another 6 months. The female is capable of breeding throughout the year, but most young are born at a time which ensures that emergence from the pouch occurs in the spring. Because of the slow rate of development of the pouch young, the female can produce and rear only one young each year.

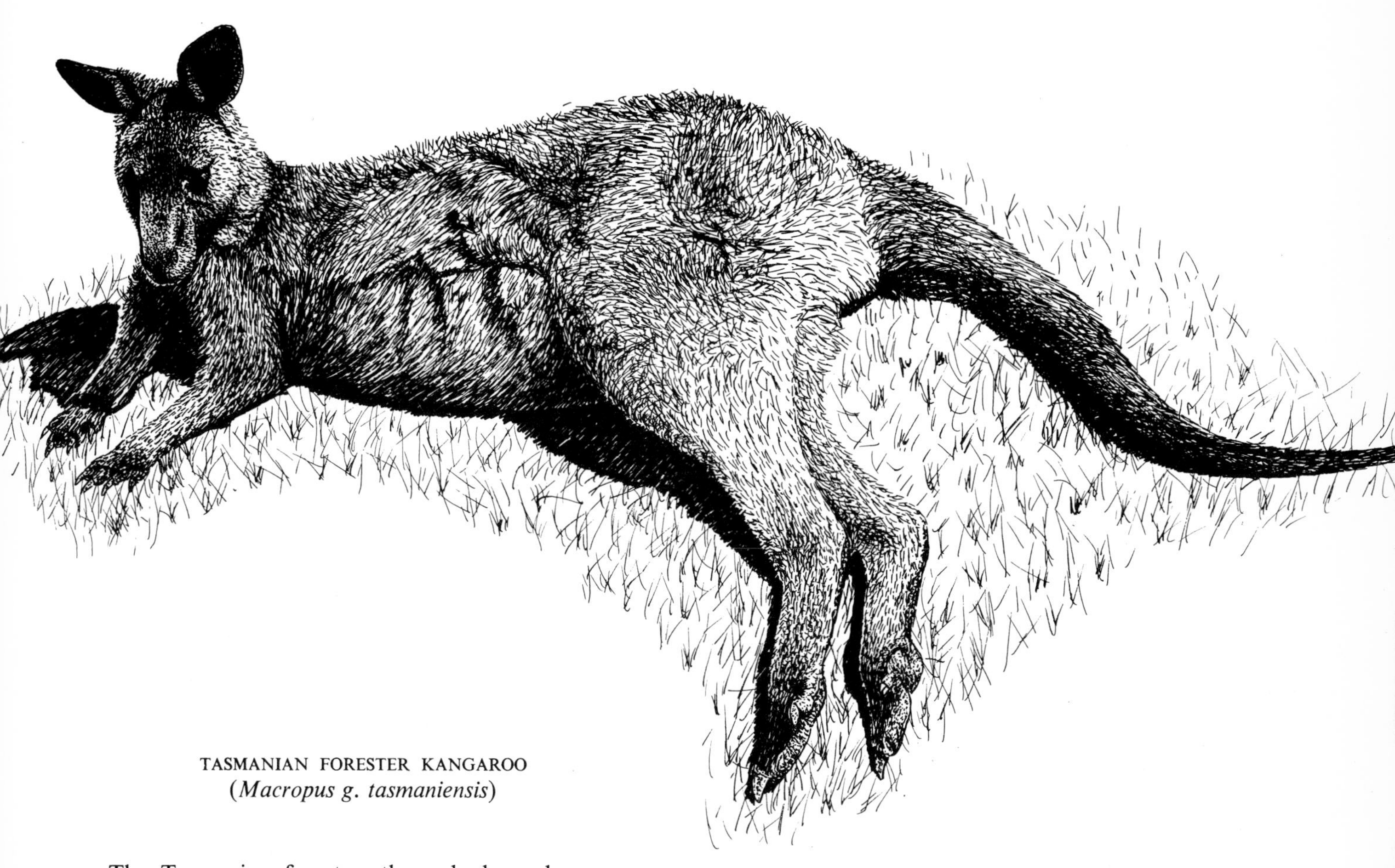

TASMANIAN FORESTER KANGAROO
(*Macropus g. tasmaniensis*)

The Tasmanian forester, the only large kangaroo found in Tasmania, is considered to be an island form of the grey kangaroo on the Australian mainland. Once widespread in Tasmania, it is now restricted to a few lightly-timbered areas of the midlands and north-east.

RED KANGAROO (*Megaleia rufa*)

This large but gracefully built kangaroo is one of the best known of the Australian marsupials. It is widely distributed in the inland of Australia, occurring throughout the plains and drier areas, usually in areas of less than 15 inches annual rainfall. It is found in all habitats except dense scrub, but appears to favour plain country with scattered trees. In eastern Australia, the colour of the short hair on the body is usually rusty red in the male, and smoky blue-grey in the female. The latter is often called a "blue flyer". In parts of Western Australia and central Australia both sexes may be the same reddish colour. A distinguishing feature of the head is a conspicuous white mark on either side of the face. The tail is grey at the base and pale at the tip.

In inland New South Wales, red kangaroos are usually found in small groups consisting of 2 to 4 animals. Occasionally large groups may be seen resting in the shade or feeding on grass. They are considered to be nocturnal animals, since they tend to avoid feeding and moving during the heat of the day, although in cool weather activity may continue all day.

The process of birth in the red kangaroo has now been observed on many occasions. After a pregnancy period of about 33 days, the female begins to clean the pouch and she may continue to do this for two or more hours before the young is born. Just before the birth the female adopts the "birth position" shown in the drawing. The back may or may not be supported against a tree or other solid object. The female in this

illustration is grasping the sides of the pouch with her fore-paws and licking the inside of the pouch before giving birth.

Although the female licks the region of the genital opening throughout the process of giving birth and during the journey of the young to the pouch, she does not lick a track in the hair for the young to follow. It is unlikely that any marsupial does so. The new-born young climbs through the hair on the mother's belly and makes its way, unaided, into the pouch. The journey takes about 3 minutes. As the nostrils are relatively large in all new-born marsupials, it is possible that sense of smell plays an important part in guiding the young to the pouch. The new-born baby of the red kangaroo, although larger than other marsupials, is only $\frac{3}{4}$-inch long and weighs about $\frac{3}{4}$-gramme, which is approximately 1/30,000 of the mother's weight.

When the young reaches the inside of the pouch it selects one of the 4 teats and takes its milk from this until it is weaned about a year later. About 4 months prior to weaning, the young leaves the pouch but continues to suckle from the outside.

Within one or two days after giving birth, the mother will mate again. The fertilized embryo is held in a resting stage in the uterus, or womb, while the young of the previous birth suckles in her pouch for about 7 months. If the pouch young is lost, the dormant embryo resumes development and is born 31 days later. Under normal circumstances a new young is born less than a day after the large young leaves the pouch. If this birth is followed by another mating, the female will have one dependent young outside the pouch, one young in the pouch and a dormant embryo in the uterus at the same time.

Female red kangaroos in captivity become sexually mature at about 18 months and males at about 2 years of age. Males and females are about the same size when one year old but thereafter the male increases in size faster than the female. At 5 years old, females weigh about 60 pounds and males up to 130 pounds. The maximum recorded weight of a male is 185 pounds.

EURO, WALLAROO OR HILL KANGAROO
(*Macropus robustus*)

The euro, which is the smallest of the marsupials usually referred to as kangaroos, has a thick-set build and coarse hair. It varies greatly in colour according to locality, ranging from grey-black through reddish-brown to fawn. The females are normally paler in colour and smaller than the males.

The range of the euro is very wide, and it is found in all Australian States except Victoria and Tasmania. It shows a preference for rough and rocky country. In New South Wales and southern Queensland it is found on the eastern and western slopes of the Great Dividing Range. In the north-west of Western Australia the euro lives in rocky outcrops in the dry plains, where the average daily maximum temperature during summer may be as high as 107° F., and on some days may reach 120° F. The animal is able to survive under these hot and arid conditions because it avoids high air-temperature by sheltering in caves, where it can withstand considerable loss of water. Both the euro and the red kangaroo require water to drink, although this may be consumed at infrequent intervals. The euro feeds during the night and seeks the shade of caves during the day. Although the euro breeds continuously in this arid country, there are responses in breeding to rainfall. In some areas, a high mortality occurs among pouch young and immature animals.

Selected Bibliography

Calaby, J. H. (1960).—Observations on the banded ant-eater *Myrmecobius f. fasciatus* Waterhouse (Marsupialia), with particular reference to its food habits. *Proc. zool. Soc. Lond.* **135**: 183–207.

Calaby, J. H. (1963).—Australia's threatened mammals. *Wildlife* **1**: 15–18.

Dunnet, G. M. (1956).—A live-trapping study of the brush-tailed possum *Trichosurus vulpecula* Kerr (Marsupialia). *C.S.I.R.O. Wildl. Res.* **1**: 1–18.

Ealey, E. H. M., Bentley, P. J., and Main, A. R. (1965).—Studies on water metabolism of the hill kangaroo, *Macropus robustus* (Gould), in northwest Australia. *Ecology* **46**: 473–79.

Finlayson, H. H. (1961).—Mitchell's wombat in South Australia. *Trans. Roy. Soc. S. Aust.* **85**: 207–15.

Griffiths, M. (1965).—Rate of growth and intake of milk in a suckling echidna. *Comp. Biochem. Physiol.* **16**: 383–92.

Hickman, V. V., and Hickman, J. L. (1960).—Notes on the habits of the Tasmanian dormouse phalangers *Cercaertus nanus* (Desmarest) and *Eudromicia lepida* (Thomas). *Proc. zool. Soc. Lond.* **135**: 365–74.

Hughes, R. L. (1962).—Reproduction in the macropod marsupial *Potorous tridactylus* (Kerr). *Aust. J. Zool.* **10**: 193–224.

Lyne, A. G. (1956).—Australian mammals. *Aust. Mus. Mag.* **12**: 121–25.

Lyne, A. G. (1964).—Observations on the breeding and growth of the marsupial *Perameles nasuta* Geoffroy, with notes on other bandicoots. *Aust. J. Zool.* **12**: 322–39.

Lyne, A. G., Pilton, P. E., and Sharman, G. B. (1959).—Oestrous cycle, gestation period and parturition in the marsupial *Trichosurus vulpecula*. *Nature, Lond.* **183**: 622–23.

Lyne, A. G., and Verhagen, A. M. W. (1957).—Growth of the marsupial *Trichosurus vulpecula* and a comparison with some higher mammals. *Growth* **21**: 167–95.

Marlow, B. J. (1965).—*Marsupials of Australia.* Jacaranda Press, Brisbane.

McNally, J. (1957).—Koala management in Victoria. Fisheries and Game Dept., Victoria. Wildlife circular No. 4.

Murray, P. D. F. (1958).—The Monotremes. *Aust. Mus. Mag.* **12**: 286–88.

Newsome, A. E. (1962).—Rabbit-eared bandicoots or bilbies. *Aust. Nat. Hist.* **14**: 97–98.

Poole, W. E., and Pilton, P. E. (1964).—Reproduction in the grey kangaroo, *Macropus canguru*, in captivity. *C.S.I.R.O. Wildl. Res.* **9**: 218–34.

Ride, W. D. L., and Tyndale-Biscoe, C. H. (1962).—The results of an expedition to Bernier and Dorre islands, Shark Bay, Western Australia in July; 1959. W. A. Fisheries Department, Fauna Bulletin No. 2, pp. 54–97. (Banded Hare-Wallaby and Little Barred Bandicoot).
Schmidt-Nielsen, K., and Newsome, A. E. (1962).—Water balance in the mulgara (*Dasycercus cristicauda*), a carnivorous desert marsupial. *Aust. J. biol. Sci.* **15**: 683–89.
Sharman, G. B. (1955).—Studies on marsupial reproduction III. Normal and delayed pregnancy in *Setonix brachyurus. Aust. J. Zool.* **3**: 56–70.
Sharman, G. B., and Calaby, J. H. (1964).—Reproductive behaviour in the red kangaroo, *Megaleia rufa*, in captivity. *C.S.I.R.O. Wildl. Res.* **9**: 58–85.
Troughton, E. (1965).—*Furred Animals of Australia.* 8th ed. Angus and Robertson, Sydney.
Walker, E. P. (1964).—*Mammals of the World.* Vol. 1. Johns Hopkins Press, Baltimore.
Wood Jones, F. (1923–4).—*The Mammals of South Australia.* Pt. I and II. Government Printer, Adelaide.
Woolley, P. (1966).—Reproduction in *Antechinus* spp. and other dasyurid marsupials. *Symp. zool. Soc. Lond.* No. 15. 281–94.

Conservation

SETTLEMENT of Australia, as of all countries, has had a profound effect on the fauna, owing to such factors as alteration of habitat by clearing, grazing by domestic animals, particularly sheep, uncontrolled fires, and the introduction of pests such as the rabbit and the fox. The Australian fauna seems to have been peculiarly sensitive to change; many forms have declined drastically and a few have become extinct. It is apparent also that some species were already declining from natural causes at the beginning of European settlement, which has hastened the decline still further.

The unique Australian monotremes and marsupials should be treasured as a national asset, and preservation of these mammals should occupy more time and thought.

Important research is being done but it is still not enough. Research on kangaroos has shown that the large numbers of these animals in the inland are to some extent an outcome of the alteration of the habitat for grazing by domestic stock, particularly sheep. In more-closely-settled areas the grazing of stock may mean the destruction of the native animals.

State fauna authorities are doing a great deal towards conservation. Strict protection of the monotremes in all States where they occur has ensured that none are in any danger of extinction. But more remains to be done. Large reserves are needed to ensure the preservation of suitable habitats for many marsupials. The animals themselves should be studied in detail so that their ecological requirements such as food, shelter, and so on, may be known. Such information would help in choosing sites for new reserves and in the management of existing ones.

Index

KOALA (*Phascolarctos cinereus*)

This attractive, bear-like animal is almost as well-known as the kangaroos. At one time koalas were widely distributed along the eastern part of Australia. They are now found in restricted areas along the coastal region from Queensland to southern Victoria. The northern koalas found in Queensland and New South Wales are smaller than the Victorian forms, and have short reddish or tawny fur. Victorian koalas are more robust, with dark grey shaggy coats. Some years ago this highly-specialized herbivorous marsupial was in danger of extermination. It is definitely on the increase at the present time, having been saved by a keen public interest and, in Victoria, by an active conservation programme.

The koala has become highly adapted to life in the trees. The hands and feet are equipped for climbing and the toes have strong claws. An interesting feature of the fore-foot is the odd arrangement of the fingers, the first and second being opposable to the rest. The tail is absent.

The food of the koala is composed almost exclusively of leaves of a few species of eucalypts, and the whole life is related to this diet. The oily leaves of these gum-trees require a highly-specialized digestive system. During the day the koala usually sleeps in a forked branch. At night, however, it becomes active and may move about. Although agile in the trees, it is a clumsy mover on the ground. Its slowness of movement prevents it from avoiding bush fires, which today are one of the greatest threats to its existence.

The koala normally breeds every year, usually producing only one young, although twins are known. The breeding season extends from September to late January in New South Wales and from November to February in Victoria. The new-born, which is about ¾-inch long, does not permanently leave the pouch until it is about 5 to 6 months old. During the latter part of this period the young leaves and re-enters the pouch at will. After finally leaving the pouch, the young koala is often carried on the mother's back until it is approximately one year old. It takes 3 to 4 years to become fully grown. Adult specimens may weigh as much as 30 pounds, but the average weight is about 20 pounds.